The M Word

Surviving Breast Cancer and Mastectomy

Susan Connell-Ford was born in North London. She moved to Ireland in 2004 where she lives with her husband on their smallholding in the Comeragh Mountains in County Waterford. Two of her daughters and her son also live in Ireland, along with four of her grandchildren.

i

The M Word

Surviving Breast Cancer and Mastectomy

Susan Connell-Ford

Whatever troubles come your way – make room for laughter everyday

Published by
Susan Connell-Ford
Glendalough
The Nire Valley
Ballymacarbry
Co Waterford
Ireland

First published 2009

Copyright © Susan Connell-Ford 2008

Susan Connell-Ford asserts the moral right to be
identified as the author of this work

A catalogue record of this book is available
from the British Library

Printed and bound in England by
Printondemand-worldwide.com Peterborough

ISBN   978-184426-619-7

Cover photography by Michael Lumley
www.aerialviews.ie

Disclaimer

The information in this book is believed to be correct but no responsibility is accepted by the author or publisher for omissions or errors. Further, the information is not intended as an alternative to conventional medicine. It does not promote any one treatment above another, and each individual should satisfy themselves as to the appropriateness of each therapy and therefore make their own informed choice. It is always advisable to take medical advice on all aspects dealing with cancer.

Thanks

Where do I start? In no particular order. Thank you so much to my family who have supported me all the way, but especially Rob for all the support, transportation, meals and technical stuff, and Esther for being there for me every day. Thanks to Mr Castineira for his surgical skills and lovely manner, to Mary for her ongoing advice, and the nurses on the surgical ward at South Tipperary Hospital, especially Gemma. Thanks to Monica for her care and support. Thanks to all in the oncology team including Deirdre, Stacia and Patsy. Thanks to Noreen who stands in for everyone and does it so well. Thanks to Eileen and the nurses on the gynae ward. Thanks to all at the Whitfield Clinic. Thanks to Cathryn, Lucy, Alex and Angela for sharing encouragement and experiences. Thanks to family and friends for making my homecoming possible, especially Dawn and Paul. Thanks to my panel of critics, Alan, Esther and Maura. And finally thanks to Theresa for encouraging me, and giving me the confidence to write this book, and to Liam, for believing in it.

Dedication

This book is dedicated to the memory of my mother, Marguerite. Passionate about the English language, she was an avid reader. Shortly before she died, she told us about a book she was reading by Jean-Dominique Bauby[1], one time editor-in-chief of a famous French glossy magazine. A stroke reduced his total physical capabilities to the movement of just one eyelid (by which means he dictated his book). It was not until after my mother in turn suffered a stroke, that I found the book and read it for myself. Monsieur Bauby's account of his illness and hospitalisation was written with humility and humour. It was probably one of the seeds that evolved into this book. Like Monsieur Bauby, my mother's stroke ended her life. She had continued to correct my speech until the day her stroke silenced her, a few months ago. She would have been proud of my attempts to write this book, though I am relieved she will never be aware of the subject matter.

Foreword
by Liam Hayes, Director of Services,
C.A.R.E. Cancer Support Centre
Clonmel, Co Tipperary

Speaking personally, I have no hesitation in recommending Susan's book as a typical road map of a cancer journey. Whilst it is Susan's personal account of her own journey, it is written honestly and without embellishment in any way, giving the reader the facts that he or she will need to know. She also addresses such issues as spirituality and peer support, showing how these assist in coping with a cancer diagnosis. Susan presents the entire story in a very readable, loving and inspiring format that will enable any person facing cancer treatment to do so with hope and confidence.

Susan wrote her book in the middle of all the 'cancer misdiagnosis scandals' and it is refreshing to read that the care and treatment she received as a public patient was timely and of a very high standard. She even goes so far as to name her consultants and nurses who cared for her so well, so the oncology team at the South Tipperary General Hospital can take a bow!

Susan is an active member of the Cancer Support Centre (C.A.R.E.) in Clonmel, Co Tipperary, and gives lovingly of her time to other members who are beginning their cancer journey. If you have received a cancer diagnosis, you can be confident that the contents of this book will ease your journey through cancer treatment and will empower you to live with cancer.

×

Contents

Contents Continued

My Story

This story is a very personal one that I initially wrote for my own benefit. At the original suggestion of my daughter Esther, on arriving home after each hospital visit, the day's events were recorded. My physical exhaustion was rarely accompanied by mental exhaustion, more like mental overtime. Once the events of the day were down in writing they felt 'dealt with'. If I was too tired to write them immediately, I mulled them over in my mind until the opportunity arose. This wasn't just writing therapy, it was also thinking therapy. Writing the story as it occurred, I didn't know if I would still be here to finish it (though I hoped I would).

The M Word is the story I would have loved to have read when I was first diagnosed with breast cancer to prepare me for the events that would follow. When several nurses suggested I make it available to other women who find themselves faced with a similar diagnosis, I filled in other details to round out the picture. If this is you, I hope my story helps you to keep coping.

Chapter 1

Retrospect

Week 52 (May 2008)

It is one year ago today since I attended a routine mammogram. Nothing suspicious was going on. No lumps or bumps (well, not on my breasts anyway!). It was just one of those appointments you have to fit into your busy schedule every now and then.

Today I am feeling pretty good. Still room for improvement but a million times better than I have felt over the past year. And tonight I have an arrangement. I am attending the cancer support centre. Tonight's meeting is specifically for breast cancer patients and survivors.

The centre is an older style double-fronted house in the centre of town. It was purchased and beautifully renovated, all from voluntary donations. We sit in the corner of the painting studio on comfortable armchairs. There is a mixture of attendees. The breast cancer survivors who regularly attend feel at home, but the atmosphere is also welcoming for newcomers.

Over the past year I have benefitted greatly from information produced by the Irish Cancer Society. A few months ago I saw a leaflet about a scheme called 'Reach to Recovery'. Tonight a visitor is explaining it to us. I have been looking forward to the talk and being able to take part.

The scheme has just been explained. A newly diagnosed breast cancer patient is asked if she would like to be put in touch with a breast cancer survivor. The 'carefully selected' volunteer is trained in support skills. She is able to offer support at each stage of treatment, if the patient so wishes, having been there herself and survived. What a brilliant idea! I note the big emphasis on 'survived'.

There are about ten of us present, but I am the only one to immediately register an interest. Well, I have been thinking about this for months now. And I certainly consider myself to come within the 'survivor' category.

I am asked when I had my surgery. "Last June", I reply. I am told I do not qualify. Three years have to elapse since surgery to qualify as a volunteer. I am not considered to be a survivor until then. I understand their reasoning but it wasn't the most tactful statement I've heard, considering the audience.

I shall have to find another channel to offer support.

And if anyone thinks I am going to spend the next two years worrying about a breast cancer recurrence, they have another think coming. Oh no, I *am* a survivor. And life gets back on track from today. Normal activities resume from today. There will be swimming, walking, art classes, training courses, family history, writing, jobs to complete, grandchildren to take out, good times with daughters, charity work. I don't have enough time for negative thoughts about cancer returning. I have a life to get on with.

~~~

6

Chapter 2

Preliminary Enquiries

Weeks 1 – 4 (May – June 2007)

"Well, that's you done for another two years".

These were the light-hearted words of the radiographer who has just completed my routine mammogram. How wrong she was! I use the word 'routine' loosely, since it was actually seven years since my previous mammogram, at which time I was living in England. Of these seven years, this latest appointment, arranged via my GP here in Ireland, was eight months in arriving. During those seven years, I had tried to organise a mammogram on numerous occasions.

I was living partly in England and partly in Ireland, having family, work and other commitments both sides of the water. The expanding routine breast screening service in Ireland had not yet reached the south east. In England, every woman between fifty and seventy years is offered a mammogram every three years. Although offered appointments there, I always found myself to be on the wrong side of the water at the appointed time. I should have tried harder.

This had been my first ever visit to Waterford Regional Hospital, a round trip of about seventy miles. As soon as I entered the building, I was reminded of Barnet Hospital in north London, where I had spent much of the previous summer visiting my dying mother. I was glad I wouldn't need to come back here for another two years.

But the next day I received a telephone call asking me to return to the x-ray department a week later for a further mammogram and ultrasound. I wasn't unduly worried. I had after all had day surgery on both breasts on different occasions in the past. Benign cysts had been removed from my left breast two decades earlier, and a polyp from the right breast, thirteen years later. I considered neither event to be that big a deal. On both occasions I had found the lumps myself during routine breast examination, and in fact now, after thoroughly checking, I was unable to even find a lump. I felt I had no reason to suspect anything sinister. Additionally, my previous lumps had been accompanied by mastitis and bleeding from the nipple, neither of which I was now experiencing. Hence my lack of concern.

The following Wednesday found me back at the x-ray department.

"You're in the wrong place" said the receptionist "you need outpatients seven. That's where they deal with breasts on Wednesday mornings."

I took myself to outpatients seven.

"You're not down on the list" said this receptionist abruptly, "and these ladies have already waited a week or two for their appointments".

I felt like a naughty schoolgirl being told off for trying to jump the queue at the tuck shop.

"What was the name of the person you spoke to?"

"I don't know, she just said it was x-ray department".

Half an hour later it had been sorted, and I was sent back to x-ray.

"It's probably nothing to worry about" the radiographer told me as she took further mammograms and ultrasounds of the upper outer quadrant of my right breast, "lots of ladies are asked to come back". I was duly dismissed and told the results would be sent through.

My personal choice precludes the use of blood. This is a decision I first made over thirty years ago. At that time I did a lot of research on the subject and came to the conclusion it was in the best interests of my health and welfare. Since then, I have continually updated my knowledge on the subject. I have found no evidence to persuade me to change my mind. I carry a signed document to this effect. Just to be on the safe side, I updated it, asking some friends whom I knew I could trust to witness this for me. Of course, they were unaware of my medical condition (as was I!)

My GP Paddy kept in contact with me and proactively chased up the results until, a week later, he rang to say further investigations were needed. He made an appointment for me to attend the breast clinic at Waterford Regional Hospital the following Wednesday. The consultant was Mr Castineira, although, according to my GP, he was also known as Mr Fiuza. He would soon become just Mr C to my family and me. Standing at the reception of outpatients seven, I was, this time, a bona fide patient, entitled to this appointment, with a letter on headed notepaper to prove it.

This is where I met Cathryn who was also waiting to see the same consultant. She was cool, calm and collected about the whole breast thing. It appeared, in fact, to be nothing more than an inconvenience in her busy life, a 'non event' as she would put it. Being a nurse, she was expecting the news whereas I wasn't. My husband Rob went to buy Cathryn a coffee. Just as he was handing it to her, Mr Castineira came out to call her in, and mistook Rob for her husband. We had a laugh. Cathryn was later sent to x-ray department for a needle core biopsy.

It was now my turn. Rob and I were first introduced to Mary, the breast care nurse. She took some details then asked me to strip to the waist and lie on a couch. She examined my breasts visually and with her hands. It felt a bit rough. I felt my breasts again. I still could not find a lump, though the upper outer quadrant of the right breast felt different from the left one.

Next, Mr Castineira arrived who also examined my breasts and performed an ultrasound scan of my right breast using a portable computer. I asked him why he had two surnames. He explained that in Spain, people take one surname from their mother and one from their father. Hoping he had a good sense of humour, I replied "that's very greedy". He smiled. He did. I dressed and sat by his desk. We waited for him to finish writing his notes.

I hadn't exactly been looking forward to the appointment. My previous experience of consultants (I only have the British health system to go by) is that many consider themselves to be god or as one book I read put it 'The Great I Am'! Devoid of any fellow feeling or bedside manner. I believe I had, in the past, been viewed as possessing only a physical body with no personality attached, and in this case only breasts perhaps. My input was not invited, my compliance expected. I am sure there are gods in Ireland too.

But Mr Castineira was different. He oozed confidence yet humility, authority yet gentleness, directness but kindness. He had great people skills despite English not being his first language, and he had a lovely smile!

"I am worried about this" he told us "I think there is a ninety five per cent chance that this is something nasty. But I won't know for sure until we perform a biopsy."

Rob likes to translate things into engineering terms.

"It's a bit like a car engine, if it's clapped out, you take it out".

"I think your wife's breasts are a little more complicated than a car engine" replied Mr Castineira.

I didn't really take it in at the time. Rob asked him about my prognosis. Mr Castineira replied it could depend to some extent on my attitude. The more positive my attitude, the better my prognosis.

This comment later had a major impact on me.

"Just one more thing" I said, producing a copy of my signed document specifying my personal beliefs. Mr Castineira was already familiar with these, and said he very rarely used blood anyway, and it wouldn't be a problem, and that should surgery be necessary, he would just have to be even more careful. That suited me fine.

It wasn't until after we had left the consultation room that the impact hit me. Rushing to the ladies, I found myself spluttered with blood. I grabbed a handful of paper towels, pressed them against my face and found a nurse.

She sat me down, cleaned me up and asked "do you suffer from nose bleeds often?"

"No, never" I replied.

I was very upset, a situation Rob finds hard to handle.

We were accompanied to the x-ray department to await the needle core biopsy. I was visibly upset when Cathryn came by. Comforting me, she described the biopsy procedure as a 'non event'. However, it wasn't the biopsy I was worried about, but the bigger picture. Cathryn and I swapped phone numbers and promised to stay in touch.

I couldn't stop crying during the hour and a half wait. Eventually I was called into a side room. Lying on a couch, I was given a local anaesthetic near the nipple of my right breast. A radiographer performed an ultrasound. Dr Wells* approached me, smiled and said "I don't think this is a tumour, I see you've had previous breast surgery and I think it's just scar tissue, but we'll perform the biopsy just in case". That made me feel much better.

He was gentle, kind and caring as he explained what he was doing, using a 'gun' to retrieve samples of breast tissue from six locations in different directions from a single surface area, the positioning guided with the aid of the ultrasound. Apart from the sting of the initial anaesthetic, I found the procedure painless. As Cathryn had said, it was a 'non event'.

16

When I left the room I was smiling.

"Dr Wells doesn't think it's a tumour" I whispered to Rob "he thinks it's scar tissue".

A look of relief came over Rob's face. As we later discovered, Dr Wells was wrong, but it did give us a week's mental reprieve.

Later that week, Cathryn and I exchanged experiences during several phone calls. Her biopsy site was bleeding, mine had healed. She had been given an appointment to see Mr Castineira the following Tuesday, I hadn't. Perhaps she had the cancer and I didn't.

* some names have been changed

~~~

Chapter 3

Diagnosis

Weeks 5 – 6   (June 2007)

$\mathcal{M}$onday was a bank holiday. I rang Mary the breast care nurse first thing Tuesday morning. The biopsy results were not yet available, so I told my daughter Esther I was free to look after our two-years-old grandson Sam for the day. Shortly thereafter, Mary rang to say the results were available after all, and although Mr Castineira officially had a few days off, he would be at South Tipperary General Hospital, at Clonmel, for a short time in the morning and I could see him around midday.

By the time Rob and I had made the twelve mile journey to the hospital, Sam had fallen asleep, so I suggested to Rob he stay in the car with Sam and I go in alone. After all, I didn't need someone sat beside me to hear that I had scar tissue!

"Is your husband not with you?" Mr Castineira asked.

I explained where he was and why. Very directly but kindly, his next words are indelibly printed in my memory.

"I have the result of your biopsy. As we suspected you have cancer and you will need to have a mastectomy."

"Now that is a shock. I wasn't expecting that".

Mr Castineira had, of course, tried to prepare me for this shock a week earlier, but I had been thrown off guard by Dr Wells' comments about the scar tissue.

It was suspected that the size of the tumour was about one to one and a half centimetres long. My first thoughts weren't about me but the implication this could have for my daughters and sisters. My eyes filled with water. We discussed the scar tissue and of course Mr Castineira was well aware of my previous surgery. I felt embarrassed that I had doubted his earlier suspicions.

He explained that my cancer was lobular, meaning it was in the lobules (as opposed to being in a duct, which is where most breast cancers are found). He drew a picture to help me understand. Evidently, invasive lobular carcinoma doesn't necessarily form a lump, (although invasive ductal carcinoma often does.) He then took me by surprise by asking "do you want to talk about reconstruction?" a subject that had not entered my mind until he raised it.

He was skilled in silicone implant reconstruction and could carry out the surgery at the same time as the mastectomy.

"Are you a 'D'?" he asked.

(When recounting this to my amply bosomed daughter Anna later, she said laughingly "what a cheek Mum, thinking you were only a 'D', I'd have been really insulted!")

Mary showed me a silicone implant. They were available in sizes A – D. The implant looked small.

At that time I felt reticent about this procedure because of the experience of my friend Anne in England. I asked if he was able to carry out reconstruction by pushing the muscle through (as Anne had later experienced) - he wasn't trained in this technique but offered to find me a surgeon who was. There was no hesitation in my reply.

"Oh no, I want *you* to do the surgery. I have confidence in you, you've been right all along, and also you respect my beliefs."

I took the opportunity to assure Mr Castineira and Mary that my decision not to accept blood was an informed one, one that I had researched and had held for many years. I continued that although I was now, for the first time in my life, faced with a situation that could be life or death, I still stood by that decision. Although I had only met Mr Castineira on two occasions, he had by now gained my complete confidence and I certainly wasn't going to entrust the removal of my breast to any old Tom, Dick or Harry!

I wasn't sure about the reconstruction. My only knowledge of breast implants was limited to the negative experience of my friend Anne. I told Mr Castineira that I didn't want the reconstruction; he said I didn't have to decide there and then but to think about it and phone Mary if I wanted more information.

I asked when he would perform the surgery, and we both got out our diaries writing in tentative dates. I asked if this could explain why I have felt so tired for the past year or so, he said it maybe could. Mary bundled some literature into my hands, and as she led me out she kept asking if I was ok. I assured her my husband was sitting right outside.

I was crying harder by the time I reached our car, but tried to hide it from Sam, who was now awake and wanting to play.

"It's not good" I told Rob, "I have cancer and have to have a mastectomy."

I didn't know it at the time, but I have since learnt of Mr Castineira's reputation as a skilled consultant and surgeon who other healthcare workers like to work with due to his caring manner with his patients and staff. Being one of the few surgeons in the area (possibly the only one) able to perform both mastectomy and breast reconstruction, I consider myself blessed that, of all the places on earth I could have found myself at this time, I was living in his catchment area.

I have three daughters. Yvette, the oldest, lives in England with her husband and two sons. Esther lives just a few miles from me with her husband and little Sam, though the family will soon be expanding. Anna lives at home with us.

As it happened, Esther worked as a receptionist for my GP. I rang her at work as she was anxiously awaiting the result. I told her briefly that the news was bad and I was on my way to her. She later told me she thought I was about to tell her I only had a few weeks to live. Note to myself to phrase things better next time. (Hope there is no next time!)

She was much too upset to continue working for the rest of the day so she took Sam from us. My GP chatted to us for a while through his lunch break. He talked positively about breast cancer treatment and this helped us put things into perspective a little. Then Rob drove me home.

I thought about my best friend Heather. Naturally, you reflect on past experiences of friends and colleagues with cancer, and make comparisons. Heather had died from what started as breast cancer about eight years earlier. She was a little younger than I was now. By the time she was aware of it her cancer had spread throughout her body. When I visited her in hospital in London, she was always positive, smiling and sharing her beliefs with others. She knew she was dying but she never talked about herself. She just looked for opportunities to help others. I thought about her husband and daughter. I had not contacted them since her funeral. I determined to correct this.

Later that afternoon, Esther arrived accompanied by her younger sister Anna. It was the first day of Anna's hairdressing apprenticeship and she had come home early because her Mum had been diagnosed with breast cancer. It was a beautiful warm day. We sat outside and cried for a while. I could handle this word 'cancer'; in the back of my mind I had known this was a possibility though I was not expecting it. But the 'M' word - that was much too big to handle. I rang my sisters in England and some close friends – I was able to tell them I had breast cancer, but I could not bring myself to tell them the extent of the surgery needed.

I looked through the literature Mary had given me. There was a CD Rom, a CD, leaflets about a local cancer support group, a book about breast cancer published by the Irish Cancer Society and a book explaining breast care services within the local health authority. The suggestion was made I should consider making a will.

Later that day, I told my daughters about Mr Castineira's comment about a positive attitude. Together we made a pact that from then on, that is how we would be. That evening we scanned the internet for details about lobular breast cancer and reconstruction. I rang my friend Anne in England - it wasn't the silicone implant that had caused her problem, but an infection.

"Come on Mum" my daughters urged, "go for the silicone, you'll be perkier than we are".

They were right. From then on, they referred to the whole affair as 'Mum's boob job' and in fact, all the information I have gathered on the subject is kept within a file of the same name. I would ring Mary the next day to tell her.

I didn't sleep much that night. There were more nosebleeds, presumably triggered by the stress, and my brain was very active. I had it on my mind to ring Mary first thing. But before I had the chance to ring her, she rang me. Since invasive lobular breast cancer may affect both breasts at the same time, I was asked to return to Waterford Hospital the following week to have my left breast re-examined.

I told Mary I had changed my mind about the silicone implant and wanted to go ahead with reconstruction. She said I'd have the opportunity to discuss this with Mr Castineira the following week.

Rob and I had moved to Ireland about four years earlier. He had somehow managed to persuade me to sell our beautiful home on the south coast of England, and buy some old derelict cottages with land in a picturesque location overlooking a valley in the Comeragh Mountains. I wasn't totally against the idea. Two of our four children were already living in Ireland. It was likely most of our grandchildren would be born there. And for me, I was returning to the land of my ancestors.

My father's great grandparents on several sides of the family had emigrated from Ireland to Liverpool, probably during the famine of the mid 1800s, as did countless other families. Several generations later, my father's family still lived a stone's throw from those same docks where they had landed. My father was the first to move further south to London when he was called up for military service during the Second World War. That is where he met my mother. My family history studies had so far taken me back to Ireland in the 1820s. So in some ways, for me, moving to Ireland was really moving back home.

However, we were living in a 200-years-old cottage. It was structurally sound, and Rob had improved living conditions no end by installing electricity, central heating and cooking facilities. But it was still quite damp. In less than four weeks' time, I would be coming out of hospital having had major surgery, but I had nowhere suitable to come home to.

For many years it had been Rob's desire to live in a remote location up a mountain track and build a house. I knew I would have to 'rough it' for a while, but I did expect my new home to be built within a year or two. Four years later, I was still trekking out to the old barn to use the bathroom. (At least by this time we had a bathroom, ducking under the plastic sheet, which served as the door, and not taking too long in the winter!)

What the cottage lacked in amenities, it made up for in views. The Nire Valley is the most beautiful location I have ever seen. We look across the valley to farmland where a few distant cottages are dotted about. To the west there is a dip in the hills, and we can just see Ballymacarbry, a village five miles away. To the east, the Nire River rises, with distant views of cascading waterfalls. The area is popular with walkers, some of whom venture through the gap to reach the lakes. I have not yet walked that far, but it is on my 'to do when I'm better' list.

Moving to the area was a culture shock. Residents would not dream of passing by a neighbour without stopping to talk. Drivers wave as their cars pass, whether they know each other or not. If there is no smoke from a chimney pot, neighbours call to check everything is alright. You could still leave your door unlocked here. It's a world my grandmother once spoke about. It's a world a million miles from my native London.

When we first moved into the cottage, the only heating and cooking facility was an open fire in the huge fireplace. That countless generations had done it before me was proved by the crane from which pots were hung. We had a family to dinner one day. There was a choice of menu. Boil in the bag chicken curry or boil in the bag sweet and sour chicken. Afterwards, the water from the pan was used for the washing up.

It wasn't that Rob had wasted those four years. It's just that he doesn't contract work out but likes to do everything himself. Our land was on a steep incline and much landscaping was needed prior to building. I left driving the JCB to Rob, but I have become a dab hand at driving a five tonne dumper. Obtaining planning permission took an age, and the bio waste system, which Rob installed in the adjoining field, was a mammoth task.

There were two buildings to erect, and Rob decided that before building the house, he would build the garage (to improve his building skills in preparation for building the house – well that was the excuse!). It was big for a garage, big enough for two large vehicles and an inspection pit with an office area upstairs. The shell was complete, the roof timbers were on, but that was it, and Rob was in quite a state about my diagnosis.

There was nothing else for it but to convert the garage into a temporary home as quickly as possible. Some friends organised barbecues for the following two weekends whilst other family and friends worked late into the nights. As for me, I spent the next two weeks choosing bathrooms, kitchens and furnishings. It helped occupy my mind whilst waiting for my first operation.

Esther bought me a book by Suzannah Olivier[2], a breast cancer survivor and a nutritionist. She explains in detail the link between diet and cancer from at least three angles; preventing the disease in the first place, reversing the condition during the early stages and (if the book was purchased too late for the above) the optimum diet to assist recovery and prevent recurrence. I took in every word. My summarising Suzannah's four hundred page book in a few sentences in no way minimises the importance I place on her advice. In fact I consider the book essential reading for any woman desiring to avoid or recover from breast cancer.

Suzannah recommends a diet very high in vegetable content (five – ten portions a day), preferably organic. Her 'kitchen sink salad' consisting of at least ten different whole grains and vegetables including some that are red, orange and purple is a daily 'must'. The diet should be moderate in seeds, fish and chicken breast, and low in dairy products and red meat. Beans, particularly soya, pulses and brassica vegetables (such as cabbage, broccoli and sprouts) should be consumed daily. She also suggests specific nutritional supplements at various stages of treatment. Esther and I decided to incorporate this into our families' diets as best we could.

Nutrition had formed part of my health and social care studies. I remembered I had studied something about a margarine/cancer link. I checked it out again. It went something like this. In order to convert runny oils like olive oil (which is good for us at low temperatures) into margarine, the oil is hydrogenated at high temperature under pressure in the presence of a metal catalyst, sometimes aluminium, remnants of which may remain in the end product, which may facilitate cancer. The process removes all protein, fibre, 95 per cent of minerals, between 65 and 100 per cent of vitamins, destroys some essential fatty acids and forms toxic substances.[3] Having converted a healthy oil into a non-healthy one, they then have the cheek to tell us their product is 'made from olive oil'.

In Mediterranean countries where heart disease is much lower than in Britain and Ireland, olive oil is eaten in its original liquid state straight on the bread. I determined to never knowingly eat margarine again.

Diet wasn't the only lifestyle change I decided to make. Although authorities differed in their views about the possibility of a connection between cancer and use of microwave ovens I decided to stop using mine anyway.[4] I changed brands of toiletries and household cleaning products to more eco friendly varieties. I learnt that most deodorants contain aluminium. This is thought to possibly be associated with the higher than average incidence of breast cancer in the upper outer quadrant.[5] Every brand of deodorant in my local supermarket contained aluminium, although aluminium-free brands were available in the health food store.

A year or so earlier, a friend, Maura, had alerted me to the dangers of Sodium Laurel Sulphate (SLS) which is found in most toothpastes, soaps and other cosmetics, used widely because it lathers easily and is cheap. It had taken my cancer diagnosis for me to take her warnings seriously. SLS is thought to have multiple health implications, but those with a connection to breast cancer are thought to be at least two-fold. Firstly, SLS is thought to have the potential to cause pre-cancerous conditions by denaturing proteins. Secondly, SLS actually mimics oestrogen, and many breast cancers are directly related to oestrogen levels (as mine was, strongly).[6]

In my quest to find a shampoo that was 'SLS-free', and after scrutinising the contents of every brand on the shelf, I spoke to the pharmacist in the local branch of a well-known chemist chain. He confirmed that all shampoos in the store contained either SLS or laurel sulphate, (which is just as bad) and admitted that these can be carcinogenic. I found alternatives in the health food store

Some research suggests that soaps and other preparations based on mineral oil or tar could possibly be carcinogenic. This was a major problem for me as I used these regularly, having received this recommendation from a dermatologist in an attempt to control my psoriasis. I managed to source soaps made from saponified olive oil, and my family switched to these until I could look into the matter further.

For some years, I had been intending to make my own soaps from pure oils such as olive and sweet almond but had never got past the recipe stage. Now I was determined to take this further. It was my intention that my home became a 'SLS-free zone'!

I also needed to lose some weight. Weight had only become an issue in recent years. I had been working in a social care agency in England which offered advice, reassurance and an emergency call out service to customers twenty four hours a day. I loved the job and was soon promoted to supervise the agency, my manager being based at another location. As the responsibilities increased, so the resources decreased, until I woke up one day to find I could no longer cope. This was followed by an extensive period of extreme fatigue.

Looking back, I don't know where the 'couldn't cope' tiredness ended and the breast cancer tiredness began, or maybe they overlapped, or the former contributed to the latter, but in any case, I had been very tired for several years. I had discussed this with my GP a year earlier; she performed extensive tests, which revealed no other causes. It was at this time she organised the mammogram.

My immune system had been complaining for some months. Since January that year I had broken out in dozens of little patches of psoriasis all over my legs, arms and body. I had suffered from psoriasis for thirty years, ever since my father died when I was twenty-five, but it had been pretty well confined to my elbows. But for the past five months, I had been smothered.

For five months my body had been telling me it couldn't cope. I had been to my GP about this on several occasions.

Although the waiting list to see a dermatologist is three years, he had managed to get me an urgent appointment (three years reduced to three days) at the local hospital, which I had attended several weeks earlier. We had something in common (apart from our interest in psoriasis!). He had worked in Southampton, on the south coast of England, close to the dermatology clinic I used to attend. The senior dermatologist back in England had invented many of the preparations now universally prescribed. It was an open clinic, you just went along whenever you needed to, and I had been a regular user for around ten years.

Back at South Tipperary Hospital, the dermatologist prescribed various treatments. He was, of course, unaware of the real reason for this outbreak – the assault on my immune system. Little did either of us know that a few months down the line, my psoriasis would disappear as a side effect of my cancer treatment.

Apart from the internet, much of the information I gained was from the Irish Cancer Society. This is where I learnt about the most significant risk factors for developing breast cancer. Some of these are considered to be: getting older, family history of breast cancer, previous breast cancer diagnosis, early menarche or late menopause, having no children or having them late in life, previous benign breast disease, hormone replacement therapy, extended use of the contraceptive pill, past radiotherapy treatment to the chest, smoking and being overweight and not physically active. I fitted into a few of these categories, yet, ironically, my two older sisters, neither of whom had developed breast cancer, each fitted into far more of them.

An additional irony is that, unlike my sisters, I had breast fed each child. This is considered to be a protective measure. Due to previous breast surgery, I was only able to feed from my right breast – yet this was the breast in which the cancer was now diagnosed.

I have always been an advocate of breastfeeding.   There is more encouragement for new mums to breast feed these days, but twenty-five years ago there was no breastfeeding lobby. Even some family members (my mother included) considered my views as radical, almost 'hippy'.   But I viewed it this way. Like anyone else, if I was out and became thirsty, I would get myself a drink. I didn't expect anything less for my babies. I breast fed wherever and whenever they needed it.   If I happened to be in a café, shop or sitting on a park bench, so be it.   I was always discreet, feeding from underneath a blouse or jumper.   I didn't go for the 'unbutton the front and let it all hang out with babies dangling' approach.

I was once attending a convention.   I was feeding my baby discreetly, when a man approached and asked if I would feel more comfortable if I went into the ladies.   I asked him if he liked to eat his breakfast in the toilet. When he replied "no", I continued that my baby didn't either.   A few minutes later, a screened off area appeared at the back of the hall, with a sign attached, announcing 'Breast Feeding'.

On another occasion, I was sitting on a park bench feeding my baby.   A Muslim lady was sitting nearby.   Our eyes caught each others'.   She lifted her hijab to show me she was doing the same thing. We smiled at each other. Two mothers in two worlds apart.

I am so proud of my daughter, Esther. She, now, in turn, discreetly feeds her baby wherever baby finds herself hungry. I have heard of people who, on entering a café, ask the proprietor if they mind if they breast feed. What on earth do you go into a café for if it isn't to give a drink to everyone in the family!

There are two circumstances in my life which I feel may possibly have contributed to my breast cancer. When I was 10 years old, our mother had tuberculosis of the lungs and since the heath test used at that time indicated exposure to TB, I received regular chest x-rays, something unlikely to be done these days. According to one study I came across, women who get chest x-rays before the age of twenty may increase their risk of developing breast cancer.[7]

I possibly may have also inadvertently put myself at increased risk as during the previous ten years, I had been treated with UVB phototherapy (the use of ultraviolet light to slow the rapid growth of new skin cells which is helpful in treating psoriasis since this condition causes skin cells to grow too rapidly.) It is believed there may be a connection between phototherapy and skin cancer and I found one reference indicating that the male genitals are highly susceptible to the cancer-causing effects of phototherapy[8] although I found no reports indicating a link with breast cancer. (An oncologist later told me there was unlikely to be a connection.)

One week on from my cancer diagnosis, and the ultrasound found no abnormalities of the left breast, though arrangements were made for a MRI scan just to be sure. Sitting in the waiting area at Waterford Hospital, I was avidly reading my book when Mr Castineira called us in. Taking a real interest in Susannah Oliver's book, he confirmed the diet to be beneficial.

He next measured me up for the reconstruction, then we had a frank discussion. My reconstructed breast would be smaller than the other one. My diagnosis of invasive lobular breast cancer of the right breast increased my risk of the same condition in the left breast in the future. There was no option but to remove the right breast, but regarding my left breast, he gave me three options: First: leave the left breast but be screened very regularly, (and be lop sided). Second: have breast reduction surgery to match the size as closely as possible to the right breast. Third: remove both breasts.

Compared to other types of breast cancer (such as ductal), women are more likely to develop lobular breast carcinoma in both breasts, either at the same time or at a later date. My research on the internet indicated my risk to be thirty per cent, although Mr Castineira thought that fifteen per cent was a more accurate figure, which figure he said he could halve by the administration of hormone therapy. A seven and a half percent risk was still too high.   I told him that although I thought he was a very nice man, I didn't want to have to meet him back in the operating theatre at a future date.

My vocabulary was increasing all the time. When cancer has developed in only one breast (as I first thought in my case), but the other breast is also removed as a risk reducing strategy, the surgery is evidently called 'contralateral mastectomy'. Sometimes women undergo the surgical removal of both breasts when no cancer is currently present. This is to help reduce the risk of developing it in the future. This type of mastectomy is known as either bilateral risk-reducing mastectomy or bilateral prophylactic mastectomy.

I didn't have to make a decision there and then, but I knew what I should do, and the decision later proved to be a good one.

~~~

Chapter 4

Surgery

Weeks 7 - 9 (June –July 2007)

Prior to my first surgery, Esther and I made the 150 mile round trip to Cork for the MRI scan. The scan involved lying still flat on my stomach, with my breasts hanging into two hollows, and being inserted into a tubular scanner for around twenty minutes. The procedure was very noisy but there was a nice choice of music via some headphones. It was simply another 'non event'.

Over the weekend I had made up my mind for certain to go for the bilateral (both sides) mastectomy and reconstruction, so early the following week I left a message with Mary asking her to advise Mr Castineira to this effect since I realised preparations would need to be made for such a lengthy operation.

That Thursday afternoon, it was back to Waterford Hospital to the nuclear medicine department for four radioactive injections around my right nipple. Cathryn had warned me this would sting, and she was right. She also warned me that my urine would be blue for a day or two! Yet another 'non event'.

She rang me that evening from the local hospital as she had been admitted to have her wide margin lumpectomy

41

performed the next day. This involves the surgical removal of the tumour surrounded by a margin (at least one centimetre) of healthy cells. I said I would try and come in to see her as I was also booked in for day surgery for sentinel lymph node biopsy.

Sentinel lymph node biopsy involves the removal of several nodes (or glands) from under the arm. Those that act as the main draining nodes for the tumour are known as the sentinel node(s). 'Sentinel' node means 'guard' node. The radioactive dye I had received the previous day would follow the path that cancer cells would take should they travel from the breast into the lymphatic system. By injecting a blue dye into the tumour, the surgeon is able to locate and remove the sentinel node(s). These would be analysed for cancer cells prior to the main surgery the following week.

(This procedure spares women the more invasive surgery involved in axillary dissection (removal of most or all nodes) and its associated side effects such as lymphoedema (swelling in the arm), although if there is evidence of cancer in the lymph nodes, axillary dissection is still required.)

Arriving at the day ward around 8.30 Friday morning, and after booking in, Mr Castineira called round to check that everything had gone as planned the previous day prior to his going to theatre. After routine questions and being labelled, the operation was explained to me again prior to obtaining my written consent.

Soon thereafter, around ten in the morning, I was wheeled down to the operating theatre. On my left, several members of the theatre team were attaching items to my body, whilst on my right, Mr Castineira was examining a scalpel. He checked with me that I still intended to go ahead with the bilateral mastectomy and reconstruction the following week. I confirmed I had not changed my mind. I remember the anaesthetic starting to go into the vein in my hand, when the next thing I knew I was in the recovery room attached to a facemask and intravenous painkiller.

Back in the day ward, I slept on and off all day. Around six in the evening, whilst waiting for my daughter Esther to collect me, a nurse took me to see Cathryn in the Surgical Ward. I talked to her for a few minutes – she was still high from the anaesthetic.

Esther cared for me in her home for the next four days. The scar under my arm was about six cm long, curved like an 'S' and very neat. The following Wednesday it was back to South Tipp Hospital in preparation for the main operation.

When I arrived at the surgical ward around two in the afternoon, there was no bed for me, so the first four hours were spent sitting in the day room. During this time "tagging", questions, chest x-ray and an ECG took place. Mary called in and showed me some photos of breast reconstructions and explained the nipple tattooing technique in which she was trained. This would be an option when the surgery had healed.

(Problem is – my sixteen years old daughter, Anna, says if I'm getting tattoos – then so is she! Although presumably not in the same place…!)

Finally, before being found a bed, Mr Castineira arrived. First he reiterated the three options. I confirmed I had not changed my mind. He then explained that there were traces of cancer cells in the first lymph node that had been removed the week before. Due to the minimal amount of cancer cells present, he had done some research as there is a variance of opinion among breast cancer specialists as to the extent of their significance. He had decided he would remove further lymph nodes during surgery the following day for further analysis.

Since this would be an additional procedure, he would start with the mastectomy and reconstruction of the right breast. Depending on the time this took, and the amount of blood I lost, he would decide whether to proceed with the left breast or whether to leave this for another occasion.

He explained that if he could only complete the surgery on the right breast, the date for the second operation would depend on whether or not I needed chemotherapy. If I did need it, the second operation would have to wait until this was complete. If not, it would be performed a few weeks later.

Additionally, in view of my decision not to accept blood, my blood volume would be increased by intravenous drip prior to surgery, so that any blood lost would be diluted. This reinforced in me the importance of having advised the consultant of any 'special requests' early on in the consultation period to give him time to prepare his strategy and incorporate this into my treatment. He then drew over my breasts with a green felt tip pen marking the areas for incision. I must remember not to wash these off.

Later in the afternoon, around six thirty, they found me a bed. I had been studying health and social care with the Open University for the past two years, and I spent the evening studying. We had discussed how social care crosses normal social boundaries. Problem is – I was not expecting to experience this from this side of the sheets.   I was intending to do quite a bit of studying during the next few weeks!

Since my last chance to eat or drink was midnight, just before this I cheekily asked a nurse if I could have a pot of tea and some toast - it tasted like heaven!   I only slept for a couple of hours that night, so I listened to some music – Divenire, by Ludovico Einaudi, my favourite artist.

South Tipp Hospital is in an elevated position overlooking the town centre. Along the far side of the town is a wide river, the Suir, beyond which is a backdrop of mountains. The town spills over up the mountain tracks. It's a beautiful view in the daytime, but at night, it is magnificent. It resembles a pool of twinkling lights, which become more sparse the further up the mountain backdrop you look.

Next morning, I was careful not to wash off Mr C's green drawing. I spent the morning reading, studying and enjoying the view.   I didn't think to appreciate my freedom of movement.   After gowning up, and answering the same questions, it was again consent time and back down to theatre.

(Coincidentally, the nurse, Noreen, who accompanied me from the ward to theatre, although Irish, had trained as a nurse at Barnet General Hospital, in north London. This is where I was born and where both my parents had died.) It was just after one in the afternoon.   This time I was given the anaesthetic before being wheeled into theatre.

I woke up in the intensive care unit (ICU) about seven hours later. The first thing I noticed was three clocks high on the wall, with no hands, then two of my daughters and my husband next to the bed. I grabbed the nearest hand.   It was my daughter Esther who, knowing how concerned I was about wanting the whole lot over and done with, said

"It's all over Mum, he managed to do both boobs".

(She later told me I moved my hand slowly over my breasts to reassure myself, then went back to sleep, which made her smile).

I was attached to four drains, a catheter, oxygen and morphine. I wasn't in pain. I just felt woozy and had blurred vision. When the morphine was later exchanged for an intravenous painkiller, I saw that there was in fact, only one clock on the wall, and it did have hands!

It felt like I had been punched repeatedly in the chest and back. Lying flat on my back, any attempted variance of position was nigh on impossible.

Next morning, ICU was the meeting place for around thirty to forty doctors and theatre staff who stood around in groups talking until each group dispersed. I was prevented from returning to the surgical ward for several hours due to the non-availability of a bed. However, when I eventually did, the movement from bed to wheelchair and wheelchair to bed was the most difficult, painful and exhausting event of the whole ordeal. I really should have been moved on a stretcher. This was no 'non event'.

It was a semi private ward. The next two days were spent flat on my back. I can repeat no better description than feeling I had been punched repeatedly in the chest and back. I was extensively bruised. The green marks had been replaced by scars, which were covered with 'stick-on' dressings. My 'breasts' felt very tight, as if I was wearing a bra that was much too small. When asked how I was feeling, I would say,

"Well, I want to take my bra off, only I'm not wearing one".

The slightest movement was so painful, even to reach out my hand to touch a controller.

I dozed on and off all day and night, but I did happen to be awake on two occasions when visitors arrived during those early days. The experience was the same on both occasions. Visitor arrives in the hallway and looks around the ward to find I am not there. Visitor goes off and is reassured I am in the ward. On her return there is a look of shock on her face as she realises it is me after all. Maybe I no longer had my breasts, but at least they hadn't removed my sense of humour.

There were three remote controls, one for the television, one to raise the back of the bed and one to call the nurse. The latter is designed with a tight-coiled lead that with the slightest movement, pings away and lands in an irretrievable position under the bed. Each visitor to the ward is requested to replace the controllers in position. Shortly thereafter a nurse, domestic or other visitor would move the trolley, which was inevitably followed by the sound of the controllers landing on the floor again.

One evening, I felt I didn't need any painkillers but I was regretting my decision by three in the morning, so I walked along the corridor to find a nurse.

"You should have pressed your alarm button", she scolded.

Well I would have done so, but it was easier to walk along the corridor than grovel about under the bed looking for it. Either there is a conspiracy amongst hospital staff or else a staff position of 'Remote Services Operative' whose job description is to ensure that remote controls remain irretrievable to patients at all times, and to monitor CCTV to record patients' frustrations! (Perhaps this is why they are called 'remote'.)

On the third day I woke to find movement a little easier, I could shuffle myself around in the bed just a little with less pain. With help to raise the back of the bed I could inch myself into a sitting position. When the intravenous drip, oxygen and catheter had been removed, I could get out of bed. The first occasion was just a few steps with the aid of a nurse.

By this time, two drains had been removed and two remained. A shoulder bag concealed the drains when I went for a walk along the corridor. On occasions, I got out of bed forgetting about the drains, but I was soon reminded by the tug on the wounds. When the lower drains were removed it was uncomfortable but not painful, and this lulled me into a false sense of security. The higher drains were inserted much deeper, and the experience of the first being removed was so uncomfortable, that, on the day before leaving hospital, prior to the final drain being removed, I asked for some additional painkillers.

Those drains caused quite a commotion amongst the nurses. Evidently Mr C, having received his training in Spain, used different drains from the other surgeons – something the nurses complained about every time they emptied them – ("those bloomin' Spanish drains"). In fact it often took two nurses to reset them using all four hands! (That was, however, their only gripe about him!)

Surgery makes you realise just how many things you take for granted. Getting on and off the loo (there being nothing to grab hold of), taking a shower or bath. Even washing - but there was a wonderful nurse called Gemma on the surgical ward – nothing was too much trouble for her – she even washed my hair – and she always had a smile on her face.

As for getting on with my studies, well, I had already asked Rob to take my books home. Towards the end of my hospital stay, a porter arrived to take me to x-ray for a liver ultrasound scan. However, the scan couldn't be performed because I was still attached to one of the drains. I later learnt it would have been impossible anyway.

By this time my left 'breast' was healing beautifully, but there was a triangular patch on the right breast along the incision lines that had formed a blister that was repeatedly drained. Each incision measured twenty-six centimetres long, starting from just under my arm and curving round under each breast to the centre of my chest.

There was also a second incision on each 'breast', starting from the area where my nipple would have been, and going downwards to meet the horizontal incision in the middle. The downward incisions were each seven cm long. It was this downward incision on the right breast that formed a blister and later split open.

The incisions were cleverly positioned. From the top there was no indication of surgery; I would be able to wear strappy tops or a tankini, and no one would be any the wiser.

There are several different methods of forming reconstructed breasts. Mine was submuscular (under the muscle). The breast tissue having been removed (Mr C later told me about ninety-nine per cent of breast tissue) the silicone implants are placed underneath the chest muscles. The newer type silicone implants, such as I received, contain solid silicone gel, which is considered safer than some earlier liquid types.

My reconstruction was performed entirely from the front. Because almost all of the breast tissue has been removed, the muscle was now located directly under the skin covering the 'breasts'. This means that when the muscles are flexed, the shape of the flexed muscles is visible through the skin (Rob says I could get a job at the circus!) However, I don't think this can be seen through clothing, though to be honest, I haven't stood in front of a mirror to check.

The feeling of wanting to take my bra off continued for several weeks, though I had no feeling at all on the actual skin covering my 'breasts', nor the area under my arm where the lymph nodes had been removed. My new 'breasts' were quite high, and I was given an elastic belt about five centimetres wide to wear – which exerted pressure down onto the silicone implants to keep them in position. I wore this for six weeks.

(On later occasions, when asked what on earth I was wearing, I would reply "oh that's to stop my silicone implants from trying to escape over the top".)

Towards the end of my hospital stay, walking along the hospital corridor one day, Mr Castineira was walking towards me. I thanked him for helping to save my life. (Looking back on this a year later, I realise my comments were a little premature.) Prior to leaving hospital, I completed a comment card singing nurse Gemma's praises, and eleven days after the operation, with an appointment for the breast clinic three days later, I went to stay with Esther for a week.

~~~

Chapter 5

Recovery and More Scans

Week 10 – 13 (July 2007)

The plan had been to help Esther that summer. She was 36 weeks pregnant, and I had hoped to take our grandson Sam out several times a week to give her some space. Instead, she was caring for me. By now movement was continuing to improve, though there was still tightness around my breasts and the feeling of wanting to take my bra off continued. I still slept a lot. A miracle happened this week. Instead of being confined to lying in the same position on my back, I was able to lie ever so slightly towards my left and right side.

The breast clinic was running late but there was quite a social event going on in the waiting room amongst several patients. Ex patients were reunited with each other and had six months' or a year's news to catch up with. I was hoping Mr C would have the biopsy results, but I would have to wait another week for these.

The left breast was continuing to heal well. On the right breast the triangular blister had now formed an open wound and Monica, the tissue viability specialist nurse (but usually known as the 'wound nurse'), arranged to clean and dress this on alternate days. Over the weekends, when Monica wasn't scheduled to work, she either went in specially or I attended accident and emergency (A&E) department.

Having been cared for by Esther for the past week, I felt I should move out as she needed to get her home ready for her new arrival. The temporary garage conversion wasn't ready so I moved up to my mother-in-law's beautiful hillside home overlooking the town, one of those distant twinkling lights I used to watch as an inpatient.

The following week was very busy, with multiple appointments. On Monday, my evening appointment with Monica was followed by a liver ultrasound. Between appointments, I bumped into Gemma (the nurse I completed a comment card about). She had a big smile on her face. My comments had first gone to the director of nursing, then back to the ward. She thanked me. We chatted for a while. She was no longer working on the surgical ward. She had transferred to coronary care, her speciality.

The radiographer I was about to meet was in stark contrast to Gemma. Her skills in using the ultrasound equipment did not extend to her people skills. Perhaps it was unusual to be running an evening clinic. She gave the impression she didn't want to be there. It wasn't my preferred way of spending the evening either.

The liver ultrasound involved lying stretched out straight on a couch. Scans were taken whilst I was in three separate positions, on my back and on each side. My movement, though improving, was still limited, and the radiographer was impatient about my slowness in changing position.

The hospital information brochure described this as a painless procedure, but I found it to be very uncomfortable due to the scanner being dug so deeply into my flesh. Definitely not a non event. And to think that I was supposed to have had this

56

scan whilst still an inpatient; this would have been impossible. As it was, it was all I could do to turn on to my left and right side, two and a half weeks after the surgery.

Next day it was back to the breast clinic. After the examination, Mr C had lots of news for me. His first comment was that the decision to remove the left breast was a good one, as there were extensive pre-cancerous cell changes that could only be detected under the microscope. Additionally, the tumour in the right breast was bigger than had been thought, around four centimetres by two. There were also pre-cancerous cell changes in other areas of my right breast. Mr C had yet to ascertain the position of the tumour; if it was close to the muscle, I may need radiotherapy.

He also gave me two cards (similar in size to credit cards) containing details of the prostheses. From now on, these would need to be carried at all times. There were a whole host of other precautions too. If ever I had a procedure such as a tooth extraction or colonoscopy (hopefully never!), an anti-biotic would be necessary as, having prostheses increased the risk of infection.

Mr C reiterated some precautions due to the axillary surgery. Medical procedures such as taking blood samples or blood pressure should only be performed on the left arm from now on. Wearing jewellery on the right hand or arm should be avoided because it could trigger lymphoedema, a swelling in the arm.

Other advice included wearing gloves when gardening and household gloves in the kitchen to avoid scratches (which can provide an entry for infection). Treating cuts and scratches immediately with antiseptic (preferably avoid getting the cut in the first place!). Protecting the affected area from the sun, avoiding use of wet razors, restrictive clothing (especially near the armpit), saunas, steam rooms and Turkish baths.

I asked Mr C whether it was probable I would need chemotherapy and radiotherapy. He felt that the former was probable and the latter improbable, and confirmed he was now referring me to an oncologist.

Next day, Wednesday, it was back to Waterford Hospital for a bone scan. It was a split appointment at the nuclear medicine department. First we attended at half past nine for an injection in my arm, then returned two hours later for the actual scan. This involved lying still on a bed whilst a camera moved slowly over me. It took about twenty minutes, and was another 'non event'. Between the two appointments, Rob and I went to see a social worker who gave me some details of wig makers, plus a prescription for a hairpiece.

On the way back to mother-in-law's home, I called into the garage that was to become my home to see how Rob was getting on. The kitchen and bathroom were installed, and beautiful wooden floors and a wooden staircase. He was just starting to put the central heating in, and there was sawdust and tools everywhere.

Major DIY and tools have been part and parcel of my twenty-seven year marriage to Rob, but this was the first occasion in all those years that I felt I couldn't cope living amidst major building works. This was also the first time I had seen my home for over four weeks.

That weekend, in the course of regular hospital visits to check the wounds, the A&E doctor was concerned that the wound on the right breast had become infected, and prescribed antibiotics (the first of many).

It was now twelve weeks since the original mammogram. At the breast clinic Mr C used a scalpel to clear away the outer layer of the wound. Thankfully I still had no feeling in this area. He expressed the possibility that the skin might not heal over the wound, in which case it would require further surgery. I asked if this was something to worry about. He confirmed it wasn't.

I had a list of questions for him. I had asked several times if my tumour was hormone receptive, and he confirmed that this was strongly the case. I had already checked out the implication of this. Five years of hormone therapy, taking one tablet a day.

Also I had wondered why there was no additional scar from the axillary clearance (in my case, removal of twelve lymph nodes). He confirmed this had been performed from the main incision.

During the week, I had developed pain from under my right arm, along the muscles down to my wrist. He demonstrated a circular motion exercise for me to practice. At this appointment some stitches were removed and a blood sample taken to check my blood count. Monica then cleaned and dressed the wound as she did every other day.

Later that week, after Monica again cleaned and dressed the wound, I went to see Cathryn as she had been readmitted to South Tipp to have the margins of her lumpectomy made wider. When Cathryn's tumour was examined under the microscope, there was not a sufficiently wide margin of healthy cells surrounding it. Hence the need to obtain a wider margin. It is quite unusual to be called back for this. We chatted for several hours and got to know each other better. I promised to call in and see her again over the weekend, but as it turned out, even though her surgery was performed early the next day, she was discharged the same evening.

Week thirteen ARM (after routine mammogram). Esther's baby was due this week but there were no signs of her imminent arrival into the world. I received the appointment to see the oncologist the following week. I had two bad days this week. I wasn't depressed, just tearful. I don't know why. Maybe it was because the chemotherapy was getting nearer and I wasn't looking forward to it.

It was back to the weekly breast clinic. Mr C again cleared away the outer layer of the wound with a scalpel. He said it was healing well. He now felt further surgery would be unlikely.

I had another list of questions. The bone scan and liver scan were both clear. I needed clarification in my mind that I had understood the significance of this, so I asked "does this mean that we are pretty sure the cancer hasn't moved anywhere else" which he confirmed. Sigh of relief. It was also confirmed that my blood count was back to normal. But it wasn't all good news. The tumour wasn't near the muscle, but it was near the skin. This meant that I would need radiotherapy after all.

Mr Castineira advised me to obtain a bottle of rosa mosqueta oil and massage one drop into each breast each day, particularly the areas of incision. I had never heard of this before, but fortunately, the health food store had. Then Rob picked me up. He was taking me to the supermarket as it was our first day in our new home.

From then on, I applied the rosa mosqueta oil every day, though I needed more than one drop. It makes the skin feel really soft and is also a lovely facial moisturiser although it can stain clothing and bedding badly. I don't like the smell, so I added a few drops of rose essential oil to the bottle. It now smelt lovely. Actually, that rosa mosqueta triggered major future changes in my life and that of Esther's.

It was a nice evening. I made a start in sorting out the kitchen cupboards, then my youngest daughter, Anna, arrived home from her week in England. Her friend Kirsty was also staying for the week. We sat around, had a drink and a laugh.

Later that week, whilst Monica was again cleaning and dressing the wound, I asked her if she thought I should wear a bra yet. This would have been impossible before now, due to pressure on the incisions. She suggested I go and chat to Mary, the breast care nurse. She took me along to her office. I was so glad I went, such a lot of helpful information came from that discussion. When I entered her office, I looked around and I went to ask Mary if this was where I had been given my diagnosis. Before I could ask her, Mary, anticipating the question, replied that it was.

We discussed bras, and she measured me. I tried on a few different styles and found one or two that were comfortable. We then discussed chemotherapy and radiotherapy. I learnt that the chemotherapy would be administered here at South Tipp on the day ward. Attendance would be for several hours approximately every three weeks where chemotherapy is administered intravenously. In between appointments blood tests would be taken to check the impact of the chemotherapy on my blood.   Based on the results the decision would be made when the next treatment would be scheduled.   It was likely that the treatment would be over four or five sessions.

Some cancer patients also attend Waterford Hospital for a day during the second week of each three weekly cycle to receive a different chemotherapy drug.   Mary thought it improbable that I would need this but she couldn't be certain - this would be up to the oncologist.   My hair would probably fall out just prior to the second three-weekly cycle.   It wouldn't fall out all in one go, she told me, but chunks would fall out at a time.

Mary also advised me that, whilst chemotherapy usually commences about six weeks after surgery, the oncologist might not wish to start the treatment until the wound had fully healed.   Once the chemotherapy was complete, I would attend a private clinic in Waterford for radiotherapy.   This would be five days a week, Monday to Friday, for about a month to six weeks.   It was really good to have this frank discussion with Mary, it prepared me for the next few weeks.

About four weeks after surgery, I resumed driving.   I was starting to get my life back again.   I had no difficulty in steering but some of the gear changes put a bit of a strain on my breasts.   And as for getting into reverse gear or changing from high to low ratio – that was a two handed job.

There were other usually simple jobs that I found very difficult, uncorking a bottle of wine (an essential occupation), slicing potatoes or carrots, changing bedding, in fact anything which required a bit of pressure.

The surgery now out of the way and with more energy than I had had for some years, I hoped the worst was over. It didn't quite turn out that way.

~~~

Chapter 6

Chemotherapy Imminent

Week 14 – 20 (August – September 2007)

I received a letter from a friend in England this week – she had experienced breast cancer seven years earlier, and her treatment included lumpectomy and chemotherapy. She sent me details of all the food supplements she had taken. She had learnt that a dosage of 1,600 international units (ius) of vitamin E daily may prevent hair loss during chemotherapy. She had only learnt this after her hair had already fallen out so she started taking 4 x 400 ius tablets spaced throughout the day starting half way through her course of chemotherapy. Her hair grew back even whilst still having chemotherapy! This would be number one on my list of questions for the oncologist on Friday.

I rang my dentist in England. I have used the same dentist for twenty years and had continued to return to England, being unable so far to find a dentist in Ireland who performed high quality preventative care. I was due to have treatment in two months time, and wondered whether this would still be possible. The dentist advised me to talk it over with my oncologist, as some doctors do not like patients to have dental treatment during chemotherapy. I was also due to be taking an exam during the same visit to England. I really needed to find out what the next few months were likely to involve, as I had some important decisions to make.

When I saw Monica later in the week, I was feeling tearful. She was very kind, bought me a cup of coffee and made time for a chat. I didn't really know why I was crying. Maybe the appointment with the oncologist was getting nearer, maybe I felt I had let Esther down by not having Sam, maybe I was just missing looking after Sam or maybe I was missing my mother. Breast cancer was the first major incident in my life I had had to cope with without being able to talk it over with my mum (though I was relieved she was unaware of this).

Monica was really sweet. She told me it's ok to cry sometimes, and that I'm not expected to feel on top all the time and probably crying was just what I needed to do right now. She said that now is not the time to be worrying about other people, I could do that next year, but now is 'me' time. It was the type of advice I had spent years giving to other people. Now I needed someone to say it to me.

Later that week, we had Sam for a few hours whilst his mum attended the antenatal clinic. It was his first lone visit since we had moved into the garage conversion. I had washed all his toys and brought them over, so he soon felt at home.

My husband Rob was different today. He had been very hurt by the actions of some friends a few days earlier, and he didn't seem to be coping. In fact he appeared to be oblivious to what was going on around him, something I had never seen in him before. I ended up doing everything at home myself.

He was feeling really stressed and not coping. He felt he wasn't safe if he went into town, only feeling safe at home. He had started to feel this way since first hearing the probability of cancer, and my subsequent nosebleeds, but he had been so busy getting our home ready, it had kept him occupied. He told me that when I was having the main operation, he was so stressed he couldn't ring the hospital, relying on our daughter to do so, and getting the information from her.

When I took Sam back to his mum, we had a chat. She had noticed a difference in her dad about a week ago. It's probable that his stress had been building up over the past three months, but the incident earlier in the week had been the last straw. The next day, I was due to attend my first appointment with the oncologist – an important appointment as I would be finding out when my chemotherapy and radiotherapy would be likely to start. Rob had been planning to come but I knew he would not be able to cope with this now. I was going to have to be extra strong, not just coping with my breast cancer. It looked like I was now going to be caring for Rob for a while rather than the other way round. Fortunately, I was feeling stronger after my surgery and the onslaught of chemotherapy hadn't yet hit me.

The next day was a big day. Amongst other things a new family member arrived, I found I had joined a new 'social club' and gained lots of important information.

I drove Anna into work early as I had appointments at the local hospital to see the oncologist and then Monica, the wound care nurse. Anna's hairdressing apprenticeship was progressing well. On the way there my son-in-law Dave rang to say he had already taken Esther into hospital. She was about to have the baby, and could Anna look after Sam. We met up with him. Rob was in no fit state to help and Anna was due to start work within an hour so I arranged for mum-in-law Marie to take over from Anna when she went into work, promising I'd be there as soon as I could to help with

Sam. I rushed to the hospital where the oncology clinic was running several hours behind schedule.

There were four or five ladies, probably in their seventies, sitting in the waiting room. The conversation was very open. I sat down with them.

"You for the cancer clinic?" asked one. I confirmed that I was and that it was my first appointment".

"What have you had done then?" asked another.

Drawn into the openness of the conversation, I replied "I've had a double mastectomy".

"But you're so young" said one of them "you expect it at our age, but not at yours".

Having explained that my daughter was two floors up in labour, they kept asking me if there was any news. Nurse Monica offered to ring up the labour ward but I knew Esther and Dave would want to tell me the news themselves. As the conversation continued, it emerged that all these ladies had completed their chemotherapy and radiotherapy and were attending follow up appointments.

Over the course of the next two hours, each lady was called by name and disappeared down the corridor. When my name was called I was taken into a side room to have my height, weight and blood pressure recorded, and then I found myself sitting with the same group of ladies, but just further along the corridor.

"By the way my name's Susan", I said.

"Oh I can never remember names", replied one, "I just remember what you've had done".

Well that will be something to look forward to next time I see any of them in town! Perhaps they will refer to me as Mrs Double M!

Today I met a lady called Lucy. Unbeknown to me, I would be seeing much more of her. She was about ten years younger than me. Her cancer was more aggressive than mine. She had had her surgery two weeks before me, but, like me, she was unable to commence chemotherapy because her wound had not yet healed. She was also seeing Monica to have her wound cleaned and dressed. I was just thinking about how nice the comradeship amongst people experiencing similar circumstances is, when I received a text message from Dave to announce the arrival of their baby daughter, Ruby. I would go and see them as soon as I left the clinic.

The regular oncologist was away. The locum was from Belgium, Brussels, spending her holiday working in Ireland to help improve her English. It didn't seem to me to need improving. She explained that the most important part of my treatment was the surgery, so the main part was already out of the way. Although the doctors were not aware of any cancer cells elsewhere in my body, they were recommending chemotherapy as a precaution. This would be administered by intravenous drip over four sessions, twenty one days apart, on the oncology day ward here at South Tipperary Hospital. My blood would be monitored in between appointments to check the impact the treatment was having on it.

The regime I would receive was called 'A/C', being the initials of the drugs I would receive, adriamycin (also called doxorubin) and cyclophosphamide. The use of adriamycin meant I would definitely lose my hair. Whilst checking out chemotherapy on the internet, I had learnt that the drug methotrexatel, which is sometimes used in breast cancer, has the (beneficial) side effect of treating psoriasis. In fact, it is sometimes used solely for this purpose. It would be great if my psoriasis cleared up as a side effect of chemotherapy.

Unfortunately, this drug was not on the agenda.

I asked about the vitamin E but was told this would not be effective with the drugs to be used. In fact they recommended I use no supplements at all during chemotherapy treatment except one multi vitamin daily. It was also confirmed that any dental treatment should be postponed until chemotherapy was complete.

Further information gained was that due to the large size of my tumour and its close proximity to my skin, (and because my skin was retained during the surgical procedure), I would need thirty sessions of radiotherapy, directed onto the site of the tumour. This would take place for six weeks, from Monday to Friday, at a private clinic in Waterford, commencing three weeks after the final chemotherapy session. She then calculated the chemotherapy drug doses.

The oncologist was hoping treatment would start the following week, however, when she examined my 'breasts' she said it would have to wait until the wound had healed, as chemotherapy would stop the healing process. As I had an appointment to see Mr Castineira two weeks later, she booked me in to start the chemotherapy a week after that, subject to his confirmation that the wound had healed sufficiently.

An echocardiogram was also ordered. I received some written details about the chemotherapy treatment and was booked in to have blood tests taken on the oncology ward the following week.

Monica then cleaned and dressed my wound. She also lent me a book that explained the healing process of wounds.

"It will help you with your book" she said.

I told Monica I thought Rob was in a bad way, and she recommended I take him to see our GP. Monica's book was very interesting. My wound had gone through several unpleasant stages but it was now mostly red which was granulation tissue, a healthy sign, as the next stage was for it to form skin.

When I told Anna about the chemotherapy, she said "Mum, can I do a few practice hair cuts on you before it falls out?"

That weekend, whilst browsing around the shops, I bought myself a hat.

The following week, back at South Tipp Hospital, after my appointment with Monica, I was on my way upstairs to see Esther and baby Ruby when I bumped into Chris, who I had met on several occasions at the breast clinic. Chris had had her surgery one week before me, and she was due to start her chemotherapy the following day. She had already got her wig, and she told me they have very nice bandannas you can try on in the oncology department! When I got home, I rang a wig supplier and made an appointment for later in the week.

After my midweek session with Monica, I located the oncology day ward. I was the only patient there as chemotherapy wasn't being administered that day. The oncology nurse, Stacia, explained the day ward set up, answered my questions in a very unhurried manner, and then took blood samples.

I asked about the bandannas, and she brought me a box full of different styles to try. These ranged from elaborate scarves to simple soft bandannas. She suggested that I probably wouldn't want to wear my wig all the time and these might be helpful for wearing around the house and at night, especially as my chemotherapy would be running into the winter months and my head would likely feel cold. I hadn't thought of that, and I chose two soft bandannas in different colours. Stacia also explained that I would have further blood tests just before and between chemotherapy sessions.

Next day, I set off for my appointment with the wig supplier in Waterford. It was a small attic room, over a doctor's surgery, with shelves of wigs in different styles and colours, comfortable chairs and a large mirror. I already knew that the proprietor Bernie wore a wig due to long-term alopecia but I was surprised she was so young, slim and attractive. Her hair looked great and I would never have known she was wearing a wig if I didn't already know. She compensated for her lack of eyebrows and eyelashes with skilfully applied makeup.

The session was very unhurried. I appreciated the privacy of being the only client there. I expressed my concern about how some wigs look so false, and she showed me how these ones were made. The 'hair' was attached to a see through micro fibre that looked very natural because the scalp shows through, so it looks like the hair comes out of your scalp. My hair was styled in a chin length bob, brown with blond highlights. I felt I needed my hair to be at least this length at the front as I tended to hide behind it when I felt uncomfortable or embarrassed about anything.

Bernie brought me about six wigs of a similar length. However, the 'bob' style wigs didn't suit me because the hair was quite thick whereas mine was fine. The last wig I tried was jet black – the top was layered but the lower layer was long. The colour looked ridiculous on me, and it was much too long, but I knew my daughter Anna would be able to cut it to a suitable style. I chose a colour combination similar to my own, mid brown, with light brown and blond highlights. I would have to wait about ten days for my wig to arrive.

When I got home there were three letters waiting for me, all hospital appointments. Two of the appointments were for the same day the following week, an echocardiogram at South Tipp Hospital and the consultant radiation oncologist at Waterford Hospital. It would be impossible to attend both on the same day. Being a cancer patient was almost a full time job. I had attended hospital appointments almost every day for the past two months. Some days there were two appointments.

Next day, after seeing Monica, I went to the cardiac department to explain why I could not attend the appointment the following week, it coinciding with another appointment. At first the receptionist seemed unsympathetic, as if I was planning on missing the appointment for some trivial reason. She told me they were down to half the usual number of staff, and there were no appointments at all for at least sixteen weeks. However, when she looked up my details on her computer, she changed her tune.

"Oh I see you are an oncology patient, I'll see what I can do".

After a couple of phone calls, I was told they could fit me in there and then. My waiting time had been reduced from sixteen weeks to sixteen seconds!

The echocardiogram involved being stripped to the waist but wearing a disposable gown open at the front. Lying on a couch, it was similar to an ultrasound scan, the scanner being moved over my stomach and around my left breast. It was dug into the scar and hurt a bit, but not as much as the liver scan. Scans were taken whilst lying on my back and on my left side.

The cardiac technician explained that sometimes she found difficulty in getting a good picture from patients who have had breast reconstruction, however in my case she could. The whole thing took about twenty minutes. Evidently I might also receive further echocardiograms between chemotherapy sessions to assess what impact chemotherapy has on my heart. Being a cancer patient was going to continue to be a full-time occupation.

I met Cathryn for lunch. My various appointments were in the forefront of my mind whereas Cathryn had other concerns on hers and hardly thought about her breast cancer diagnosis. Her appointment for the breast clinic was several weeks away and she had no other appointments.

"I envy you" she said "you know exactly what's going on and you have it all planned out".

Next day, I took Anna to work then went to the supermarket. Up until this time, since my operation, I had done just a little shopping at a time, but today I did a full week's shopping. I could hardly steer the trolley back to the car and really couldn't cope with lifting out the shopping, (even though I did it one item at a time). I got quite upset, thinking that Rob should really be with me helping, although I knew he couldn't have coped with being in the supermarket.

I sat in the car for a while. My breasts really ached. Since my operation, this was regularly how they felt when I was overtired. I drove home. I left my shopping in the car and went straight to bed and slept for about six hours although it was the middle of the day. I still experienced the 'I want to take my bra off' feeling but not quite so badly, and when I felt tired, my 'breasts' felt heavy. There was still no sensation when I touched the skin on my 'breasts', and it was still numb under my right arm.

I like to sleep on my stomach. Whereas real breasts are squodgy and mould themselves around the pillow, reconstructed breasts are stiffer and sit firmly forward in place, and it is more difficult to get comfortable. Cuddling lots of plumped up soft feather pillows helps.

They do have their advantages though (the breasts, not the pillows!) They are cosmetically very pleasing, (which Rob has his own way of summing up), sitting firmly in place without the need of a bra. I did try wearing a bra the previous week but found it caused redness around the incision wounds, so I had reverted to wearing soft cotton spaghetti strap vest tops for the time being. Additionally, compared with the genuine thing, reconstructed breasts are more comfortable when 'off-roading' something we have to do to reach our mountainside home – as they (the breasts) don't bounce all over the place!

Reconstruction sometimes includes the formation of nipples from skin taken from elsewhere on the body. I wasn't offered this procedure, but, to be honest, I am quite happy not to have nipples. I have always disliked them being visible through clothes, something I don't have to cope with now. This would also be an advantage of the nipple tattoos! (There is also a 'stick-on' variety! My friend Anne used to use one of these. On waking in the mornings, she and her husband played 'hunt the nipple'. It could be found anywhere such as on her knee or his shoulder!)

If chemotherapy was to stay on track, I had just over a week for my wound to completely heal. The week after next, I had appointments for the breast clinic and medical oncologist. I hoped the chemotherapy would be given the go ahead - I was anxious to get it out of the way.

My final week before my appointments with the consultants had arrived. On Monday, when Monica cleaned and dressed my wound she was very pleased with what she found. Skin had started to form all around the edge - in fact the wound was now down to about half its original size. She sought the opinion of another nurse, and together they felt it would take another two or three weeks to fully heal.

Tuesday, it was back to Waterford Hospital to see the consultant radiation oncologist. (The medical oncologist deals with chemotherapy whereas the radiation oncologist deals with radiotherapy). I was photographed, asked about my medical history and then examined. He commented on the neatness of my reconstruction, describing the procedure as a 'skin-sparing mastectomy'. He continued that due to the large size of the tumour and the inability of the surgeon to obtain a wide margin due to the tumour's closeness to my skin, I would require radiotherapy over the whole of the right breast area. This would commence three weeks after chemotherapy is complete, and I was requested to ring the clinic on the last day of chemotherapy treatment for the ball to be put in motion.

At my first radiotherapy appointment I would evidently have a simulation planning scan which measures the area to receive the radiotherapy to ensure the whole of the area receives treatment. I would likely receive twenty-five radiotherapy sessions, every day, Monday to Friday, for five weeks. Side effects might include a 'sun burnt' skin and tiredness.

For three years before my breast cancer diagnosis, I had been studying health and social care, though I had been involved in this work for many years. I knew I wanted to put my studies to use, but I wasn't sure how. Reviewing some of the literature I had collected since my diagnosis, I came across a leaflet produced by the Irish Cancer Society *Reach to Recovery*. The charity train (carefully selected!) volunteers who have themselves had breast cancer to provide advice and support to other women who have recently received a breast cancer diagnosis.

Maybe this is the area I should pursue. I did realise however, that I would be unable to empathise with women who had not had reconstruction and needed advice on 'external' prostheses, bras and swimwear. One thing I knew for sure was that, with the treatment and support I had received so far and was yet to receive, I had a huge debt to society (which debt I could never repay).

Rob was still very stressed. He agreed to go to see our GP the following day. This is a turnaround of events. An engineer, he is familiar with all things practical but few things emotional, whereas I, I have the ability to experience the full range of human emotions! We will call in to the GP on the way to see Monica at South Tipp tomorrow.

It was now eight weeks since my surgery. The bruising had gone and the incision scars were not quite so prominent. I discovered I had a little feeling around the edge of my 'breasts' though most of the surface was still numb, as was under my right arm.

It was the end of August. It had been a very wet cold summer but the last few days had been sunny. I have always loved being in the sun, until this year, when I have avoided it. But I really felt like sitting in the sun for a while and oh boy – did I enjoy it – the first time this year. I was careful not to stay out too long as I had been warned not to allow my skin to become burnt, especially my right arm.

The following week I receive a phone call from Bernie of Wigs Medical. My wig was ready, so we drove down to Waterford to collect it. When I got home, I tried it on, with and without hats. It looked nice with hats. I had another 'coming out' to face. I thought about how people 'come out' for all sorts of reasons when they have had a change in their life. My previous 'coming out' was facing people after the reconstruction. They smile and talk to you sweetly, but you know full well they want to see the result of the reconstruction at the first opportunity. It was the same just after the diagnosis, when I met friends in the street, their eyes glanced down and back up again. Next 'coming out' would be publicly wearing the wig.

It was a bank holiday in England, and I thought about my mum. It was a year ago to the day since she had died. During the ten weeks she was ill, I had flown to and from London several times and stayed in her flat so I could visit her each day in hospital. On the last occasion I was due to visit her before I flew back to Ireland, I was unable to get to the hospital because I had hurt my back. I felt bad because I had said "see you tomorrow" the previous day. I had told her I loved her, but I wanted to tell her again. She died a few days later. Since then, on every occasion I see or speak on the phone to any of my family members, I tell them I love them.

That evening I received a phone call from friends who had also moved to Ireland. They are very much into healthy and eco friendly living and expressed surprise that I was following the chemotherapy and radiotherapy routes. They believed there were alternatives and expressed this strongly. One of the regimes they favoured was eating apricot kernels that contain laetrile sometimes known as vitamin B17.

It was a subject I had researched and decided not to incorporate into my treatment at this stage. They tried to persuade me otherwise. In addition to the trauma of the treatment I was facing, I found myself feeling I had to justify my decisions about it. No one should have to do this. My decisions were informed ones in as much as it is possible to inform oneself in the limited time between a cancer diagnosis and treatment. They were based equally on my consultant's advice and my own research.

It is easy to feel strongly about subjects – until it happens to you. I suppose I had also to some extent previously been guilty of this myself – having strong opinions against silicone implants – until I needed one (or two) myself. But by now I was so glad I had the breast reconstruction – it had helped me to deal with the mastectomies and to feel no less of a woman. However, I would never have tried to influence another individual's personal decision.

This phone call was unexpected. It was quite unsettling. I resolved to never pressurise others in decisions they make. Present the facts, yes. Pressurise, no. I know it was a bit naughty but I said to him "if I follow your advice but die, is it ok if Rob sends you the funeral bill?" They didn't mention it after that.

There are widely differing views on the efficacy of using apricot kernels in treating cancer. Its use is illegal in many states of the USA where doctors say that apricot kernels and other foods containing laetrile, being full of cyanide, will prove fatal if eaten.[9] However according to its advocates, laetrile is a highly selective substance that attacks only the cancerous cells. Advocates further believe that when laetrile is eaten and absorbed by normal cells, an enzyme called rhodanese detoxifies the cyanide, which is then excreted through the urine.[10]

Whilst I had decided to follow conventional treatment for my cancer at this time, I wasn't ruling out the possibility of using apricot kernels in the future should all else fail.

As it happened, for the past couple of weeks, people kept telling me how well I looked. Since recovering from the operation, about two months earlier, I had had lots more energy - more energy in fact than I had experienced for about four years – and I think that this, coupled with the diet – had really made a difference. The few days of sunshine had helped too.

The next day was an important one – it was my first appointment at the breast clinic for a month – I should have started chemotherapy by now, I just wanted to get it over and done with – and I was hoping Mr Castineira would be pleased with my progress.

He was. But he still felt my wounds would need another month to heal. This was disappointing. He said he would, however, talk to the medical oncologist the following day. In any case I had an appointment with this consultant the following Friday.

Every Wednesday, all the consultants got together and held a case conference about each patient to ensure each individual's treatment is tailor-made and nothing is overlooked. (This is why, the day following my original diagnosis of breast cancer I received a phone call asking me to return the following week for further tests to my left breast.) I found this arrangement reassuring. And that the treatment is co-ordinated amongst all consultants concerned was confirmed by the fact that each consultant explained how their particular therapy fitted into the overall treatment plan.

I had another question for Mr C. If, after the chemotherapy and radiotherapy were complete, I was to receive hormone therapy for five years in order to counteract my strong oestrogen presence, how could I protect myself from osteoporosis? (Many women my age are given hormone replacement treatment that promotes bone density, I was being prescribed the opposite.) He explained that, prior to any hormone treatment, a scan is given to measure bone density. Throughout hormone treatment, this is periodically repeated. If necessary, medication is given to promote bone density. He also advised me that weight bearing activity, such as walking, gives further protection.

Monica then cleaned and dressed the wound. Monica was my main contact at the hospital, I saw her more than anyone else. Whenever I was sitting in the outpatients waiting area, which was quite often, if she walked by she always came over to talk to me. She always made time to talk to me when I was feeling down. Funny how things like that are important when we feel vulnerable.

"I shall miss you when this wound has healed" I once said to her.

"I shall still come and see you when you're on the oncology ward" she replied.

Later that week, I was looking through my 'boob job' file when I came across a leaflet Mary had given me when I was first diagnosed, produced by a local cancer support group. I rang the number, and was invited to a meeting at a local hotel the following Tuesday.

Later that week, I had an appointment with the medical oncologist – I had only met the locum so far.

"How would you feel about having six months chemotherapy instead of three?" he asked. "Although there were only traces of cancer cells in the lymph node, I think you would benefit from a course of taxol after the A/C chemotherapy is complete".

I said I was in his hands and that I would go along with whatever he recommended. He examined my wound, and said we could start chemotherapy now but he would like to wait two more weeks.

One of the side effects of chemotherapy is to reduce blood cells. When I mentioned I had always had a low platelet count he checked my records. Normal platelet levels are between 150 and 400. My friend Angela's GP considers her count of 160 to be low. My platelet count was usually around 140 as it was currently but it had dropped to 70 after my surgery. (It later fell to 48 during an infection.)

He said they would keep an eye on it, and in any case, I wouldn't be given chemotherapy until the count was at least 100. He explained that in the very unlikely and rare event that platelet count drops very low, a platelet transfusion is given. I told him about my personal beliefs, and that a platelet transfusion was not an option for me. My reply took him by surprise. He looked uneasy. I was too.

Incidentally, Rob and I have an incompatibility in our blood that could result in a health problem for our children in uterus. Eighteen years ago, after experiencing a miscarriage, doctors in the UK tried to persuade me to have an injection called anti-D, to prevent such a problem in the future. We declined the anti-D because it was taken from someone else's blood. The doctors assured us that it was impossible for me to contract any disease from anti-D. Not wanting to put the health of a future child at risk, my blood was thoroughly screened before I became pregnant again. (A healthy Anna was born a year later.)

When we moved to Ireland five years ago, there was an advertisement in the local paper advising patients who had contracted HIV from anti-D or factor H that they had a limited time period in which to claim compensation from the government!

It was a bad weekend. I felt quite low. I told Rob about the platelet conversation and that made him feel even worse. I rang my children's grandfather as he is quite knowledgeable on non-blood medical techniques – he later emailed me some information about various alternative medical techniques that stimulate platelet production. On the Monday morning – still feeling down – I booked in to see Monica to have my wound dressed. I waited for an hour – then enquired – then another hour – then enquired again – to be told she was off sick.

I decided to go and see the oncology clinical nurse specialist who had been present at the appointment the previous week. I was crying though I did not know why. She was very sweet – she said lots of people feel down at this time – as the chemotherapy is getting nearer - it confirms the reality of the cancer. She said I had enough to cope with at the moment without worrying about something that probably wouldn't even happen. She suggested I just concentrated on coping with the chemotherapy – and if my platelet count dropped – let them worry about that. She assured me they would respect whatever beliefs I had – and they just wanted me to get better. I felt a lot more settled after that.

Next day, I was on my way to the cancer support group meeting at the hotel, when Mary rang to say Monica was off sick all week, so I arranged to call into the clinic later to collect some dressings. At the hotel, I was expecting five or six people meeting in the corner of a bar, but in fact there were about forty of us and it was a presentation to the lady who had started the cancer support group about five years ago. They had recently purchased a property and building work was due to be completed within a few weeks. When open, the centre will offer many facilities including a drop in centre, art classes and reflexology.

I met several ladies who had survived breast cancer (it was really good to hear how they had coped with the chemotherapy) but I was particularly pleased to meet a lady who had had the same type of cancer as me, invasive lobular carcinoma. She had completed her six months of chemotherapy, same drugs as I was due to have, and her five weeks of radiotherapy. She was now attending the oncology day ward every three weeks to receive herceptin. This is administered in the same way as the chemotherapy drugs. She explained that the tumour is tested for its HER2 status, and if positive, a year's course of herceptin is prescribed. This was a subject I knew nothing about. Another question for Mr C.

After the meeting, I called into the breast clinic to collect the dressings. I saw Lucy – she was due to start her chemotherapy that week. Due to an absence of available veins, Lucy had had a port inserted near her collarbone, through which her chemotherapy would be administered. We had quite a chat – she told me she had eighteen months of chemotherapy, A/C and taxol (like me) then a year of herceptin. She was participating in a trial for one of the drugs. I put a note in my diary to ask Mr C about my HER2 status at my next appointment.

When I got home, there was a letter from the oncology nurse containing a prescription for three doses of an anti-emetic (anti-sickness) drug – and a note to say I should take one dose on the morning of my first chemotherapy session (the other two doses are taken the following two mornings). Chemotherapy was getting very close. That weekend I bought another hat – and some big earrings to distract attention from my forthcoming lack of hair.

Rob was feeling a bit better, enough to go shopping anyway. He really wanted to shelter me from society for the next six months, doing the shopping etc, so I did not have to come into contact with anyone. I appreciate that it was concern on his part, but it was approaching over-protection. The information the hospital provides does say to avoid crowded conditions, particularly people who are ill - but I just had to be out and about – being shut in means not living – it would be bad enough being physically ill let alone the additionally psychological trauma of no social life.

It was mid September, ten weeks since my surgery. Monica had been away for nearly two weeks. I checked into outpatients but she was not due back to work until the following day. As previously arranged, I went to the oncology day ward. This had been relocated since my last visit. Newly decorated and newly furnished. The nurses checked my wound – they felt it needed another week, so we arranged that I would call back on Friday to have blood samples taken, and for a decision to be made whether chemotherapy could start the week following. Time was dragging on.

The oncology day ward had about eight day beds similar to dentists' chairs, the patient being able to raise and lower the back and foot rest. Opposite me was an elderly man receiving chemotherapy. Noticing he still had his hair, I asked him if this was his first session.

"No, it's my nineteenth", he replied.

He told me he had never lost his hair, though he did lose his beard for a few months. Before leaving the ward, I chatted to him and his wife.

Next day it was back to South Tipp to see Monica.

"I'm so pleased to see you" she said as she approached me.

She had just come down from the oncology ward to find out about my progress. Not having seen the wound for two weeks, she was surprised how small it was now. Hopefully on Friday I would be told that chemotherapy could start next week.

My daughter Anna had completed her haircutting course but wanted to practice an inverted bob. I was the guinea pig. She left my hair quite long at the front, (so I could still hide behind it) but cut the back quite high into a V shape. It was the first of her 'mum, it's going to fall out anyway' cuts. She did it really well, it was a shame I wouldn't have it for long.

I asked her if she could cut my wig into this style. She felt nervous about this, but said she would find out about how to do it. Next it was her sister's turn, whilst I looked after Sam and baby Ruby. I realised what a lot I had to live for.

Later that week, Cathryn rang me. She had had her radiation simulation scan, and was due to start radiotherapy the following week. Like me, she had an appointment at South Tipp Hospital the following day, so we arranged to meet up for coffee. It was now week eleven since my surgery, and I was expecting to be told we would start the chemotherapy, but the oncology nurse said she felt the wound needed another week, but we would definitely start a week on Monday.

Although the wound now only measured a few millimetres, it was still quite deep. I was, however, given a prescription in preparation for the following week so, while I was waiting for Cathryn, I walked to the chemist.

There were seven items, four to help prevent sickness, one to prevent ulcers and two mouthwashes. Cathryn was sitting waiting for me when I arrived back at the hospital and we walked to my car which was parked at the furthest point in the car park.

Why ever did you park here?" she asked.

It was to help increase my weight bearing exercise, I replied. We had lunch together. Cathryn had just had her liver scan and unlike me, had not found it uncomfortable. She was due to start her six weeks of radiotherapy the following Monday, and she had already started her hormone treatment.

Twelve weeks after surgery, I again attended the oncology day ward. My wound was photographed, blood tests were taken and it was confirmed chemotherapy would start the following Monday. At last.

What an irony! Anticipating something so traumatic, wanting something to start but knowing that the side effects would be overwhelming.

The usual oncology nurses were away, and Noreen was standing in. I had met Noreen previously as she also worked on the surgical ward. She went through the medications with me, explaining what I should take and when. I made a chart and wrote it all down.

Three other ladies came to the ward while I was there. They had all lost their hair. Two were wearing wigs, and one a bandanna. Two of them were much younger than me. I was not sure if I would have the courage to wear my wig – and if I did, I thought I would want to wear a hat as well, just so no one could see the wig!

Eight weeks earlier, I had named this chapter "Chemotherapy Imminent". Now, six weeks behind schedule, it really was.

Later that day, I bought another hat. I am not a hat person. I have probably only bought one in my life. Until now.

Having recovered well from the surgery, I was feeling pretty good. I had more energy than I had had for several years. I was out and about regularly and particularly enjoying the company of my grandchildren. I had no idea what was about to hit me.

~~~

Chapter 7

Chemotherapy – Cycle 1

Week 21 – 24 (Late September 2007)

I wasn't nervous over the weekend and I slept well the night before. Monday morning arrived. I took one Emend 125 (aprepitant) capsule before going to hospital. Rob and I arrived at the oncology day ward around eleven. The oncology nurse, Stacia, explained everything she was doing. I was to receive my chemotherapy intravenously (injected into a vein or by drip infusion).

First she brought over a box of ready prepared equipment. Unable to raise a vein in my left hand, I placed it in hot water. She then inserted the cannula – a small tube inserted into a vein in my hand through which chemotherapy can be administered by injection or infusion.

The first infusion was saline to wash out the line. Then I was given a steroid infusion, to help prevent sickness. This took about fifteen minutes. The line was then washed out with saline again. Next the adriamycin was administered. This is the culprit that was responsible for my impending hair loss. It was a red fluid contained in two syringes. One at a time, Stacia slowly administered the adriamycin from the syringe through the cannula. The fluid was cold as it went into my vein. The line was then flushed out with saline solution again.

Next I received an infusion of a bag of cylophosphamide. The whole thing took about two hours.

Whilst receiving the cyclophosphamide, Stacia went through all the drugs with me explaining what I should take and when. I had been given a prescription for seven different drugs. I had them with me and she showed me what was what. She then made us tea and toast. What a love!

The day ward had eight beds, three of them were occupied. They reminded me of dentist's chairs. Another lady, Avril, was receiving her first dose of chemotherapy, A/C, the same as me. The third lady was Chris who I had met previously in the breast clinic. She was due to have her third chemotherapy the next day. Today she was attending for blood tests. Chris was wearing a bandanna. They were both so cheerful. Patients receiving chemotherapy appeared to display a much sunnier disposition than the average person I saw walking down the road.

There was a choice of two routines. Blood tests are taken prior to each session of chemotherapy. This is to check the blood levels are high enough. The treatment is given on a three-week cycle. I could either attend early Monday morning for blood tests, 'hang around' town for two hours for the results, and then return to the ward to receive the chemotherapy, or else return the following day. We opted to get it all over and done with on the same day (though we later changed this).

I was given an oncology passport. (After all they wouldn't let just any old person in here.) On each visit, dates of treatments, details of drugs prescribed, blood test results and details of future appointments were written in. I later discovered there would be many more visits in between. The next scheduled blood tests were in ten days' time. At this point the chemotherapy would have had the most impact so blood levels are at their lowest. There were also hospital contact numbers, the local oncology ward during the day, and Waterford Hospital at other times. I was assured I could ring at any time if I was worried.

When I got up from the bed I felt a bit tipsy - like you feel when you have a glass of wine on an empty stomach - which is very annoying, not having enjoyed the glass of red wine! Not that I could have faced a drink right then. We called into a garden centre briefly on the way home to buy two fig trees. I still felt dizzy and was glad to leave. This is out of character for me. I love to be out.

When I got home, I just lay on the settee for the rest of the day and went to bed early. About four o'clock in the afternoon, I started to get waves of pain in my stomach. Each wave of pain was accompanied by nausea, which came and went with the wave of pain. It was not severe pain, but uncomfortable. Similar to period pains.

During the evening, I rang the hospital for advice. The oncology day ward at South Tipp is only open Monday to Friday nine to five so I rang the regional hospital at Waterford. I had been given some additional pills, motilium (domperidone) to take 'as and when' I felt sick and the nurse advised me to take one of these. She said to attend the A&E department if I was in a lot of pain during the night. The night was uncomfortable. I woke up a lot and felt pretty sick. I tried to vomit on several occasions, but was unsuccessful.

The next day ('week one, day two') I felt very tired and stayed in bed more or less all day. I was due to attend the Breast Clinic in the afternoon, but cancelled the appointment. I was not hungry, eating just a slice of toast and some sips of water all day. I was supposed to be drinking a litre and a half of water each day. This was going to be difficult. I could not face anything else. During the evening, I felt a little better. I actually got up for a while and rang Cathryn, apologising for not seeing her at the breast clinic earlier. I even got my mind round a bit of typing before going back to bed.

Wednesday I was still very tired. I stayed in bed most of the day, sleeping on and off. This was the last day of scheduled steroids and anti-sickness medication.

Something amazing happened that day. My patches of psoriasis disappeared, leaving dark brown skin underneath. Thirty years of psoriasis gone in two days. The oncology senior registrar had told me this was a possibility, but that the psoriasis was likely to return with a vengeance after completion of treatment.

Thursday, around lunch time, I came over very weepy and had a good cry. They had warned me about this. It seems the steroids give a feeling of well-being, which goes when you stop taking them. I felt tired and had heartburn all day (very unusual for me). I only woke up a few times that night.

Friday morning, I was feeling very woozy and had bad heartburn again. The last thing I felt like doing was going out, but I needed to go to South Tipp to see Monica. I hadn't had my wound checked for several days and Monica was due to be away the following week. I saw her around lunch time. My wound was still healing well though she gave it a little help, by cleaning it and changing the dressings.

They were also running an oncology clinic. I explained how I was feeling to the oncology nurse. My blood pressure was taken. It was very low. The doctor examined me. She prescribed an antibiotic, just in case I was sickening for something, plus something to help the indigestion. I had an extra blood test. If it showed signs of neutropenia (low white blood cell count), I would be asked to stay in hospital overnight. The results would take two hours, so we went into town for a bite to eat. During the afternoon the oncology nurse rang to say the blood tests were just within the limit so it was back home again.

October is 'breast cancer awareness' month in Ireland. There was a pink caravan parked in the shopping centre. I obtained more information which helped me better understand the side effects of chemotherapy.

Cancer is a disease of the body cells, and chemotherapy drugs are cytotoxic – they kill cancer cells but unfortunately, they kill some healthy cells too. Cancer cells divide rapidly, and chemotherapy drugs kill rapidly growing cells. Cancer cells are unable to repair the damage but healthy cells usually can.

The healthy cells most likely to be affected by chemotherapy drugs are those that normally divide and grow rapidly. This is especially the mouth, digestive system, skin, bone marrow and hair follicles. So these are the areas where side effects are often experienced.

One of the side effects to my skin was welcome – my psoriasis had almost totally gone. Although I could feel a change in the surface of the roof of my mouth, I did not experience mouth ulcers as many oncology patients do. Regular teeth cleaning, mouthwash and anti-thrush mouthwash is a part of the daily routine. I could feel the effects of the attack on my digestive tract cells, as I had a feeling of heartburn, and in fact, after swallowing food or drink, severe discomfort from my throat to my stomach.

The effect of chemotherapy on the bone marrow can result in a lowering of the number of the three types of blood cell, red, white and platelets. Lowering of red blood cells can cause anaemia; fortunately this did not occur in my case. However, my white blood cell count fell drastically putting me at risk of infection and I needed to keep a check on my temperature.

Other advice given was to avoid close contact with people with colds or other infections and to wash hands regularly. I also carried a bottle of antiseptic antibacterial hand cleanser around with me and used it frequently. Infection can be a serious complication of chemotherapy.

Although I had previously been worried about my platelet count (it being lower than average), this only fell to 97 on day ten (platelet count needs to be above 100 for chemotherapy to go ahead). The effect of the chemotherapy on my hair follicles would soon become evident and a constant reminder throughout my treatment.

The fatigue and low blood pressure continued for about a week. 'Cycle one, week two' was much better and I could not wait to get out. My hair was due to start falling out any time within the next ten days. I decided that if I was going to be shorn, I was going to do it, and not the chemotherapy. So Anna cut my hair very short all over (another practice session for her). On day ten, it was back to the oncology day ward for blood tests. The nurses didn't recognise me until they heard my London accent.

During the afternoon, Deirdre rang to say I have neutropenia and I will need to take a course of antibiotics. My neutrophil level had fallen from 4.6 to 0.3. (Chemotherapy is not administered until the white blood cell count has risen to at least 1.5). I reminded her I was already taking antibiotics so we agreed I would return the following Tuesday to have my blood levels tested again.

From this point on, for the following few months, my life revolved around the chemotherapy cycles. How I felt, what I could do depended on where I was on the cycle. Each cycle of chemotherapy had a 'week one' (when I actually received the chemo), a 'week two' and a 'week three'. These were expressions regularly used with my family. As in "hey mum, it's a 'week three' next week. Shall we go out somewhere?"

By the end of 'cycle one, week two', I was feeling really good, quite energetic and really enjoyed meeting up with my daughters and grandchildren for coffee. If chemotherapy was going to mean one bad week in three, I could cope with that. However, breast cancer continued to be a full-time occupation, with hospital, GP and pharmacy visits in preparation for round two.

'Cycle one, week three', and I was feeling really good. My wound had almost completely healed and I felt great. On Tuesday, it was back to the breast clinic. The nurses were comparing my now healed breast with photos from my file. When one nurse said "himself will be pleased" I realised that 'himself' was the general term the nurses used for Mr Castineira.

There is a safe feeling about attending the breast clinic. The same nurses are in attendance each time, and I feel I'm in good hands. Also, Mr C always sees all of his patients personally. I had a couple more questions for him. As usual he found time to answer these in an unhurried manner. I asked if there is a 'best before date' for the silicone implants. His reply was that if I should receive any trauma to the chest, they should be checked. Other than that, they will be checked regularly after ten years. There is unlikely to be any leakage due to the 'gel' nature (previous ones were liquid), but should that occur they would need to be replaced.

He also checked my HER2 result, which was negative. This was good news. I would not need to be on the drug herceptin for a year.

Having attended the breast clinic so frequently, my next appointment, four months away, was reassurance for me that, surgery-wise, things were going in the right direction.

Attending the breast clinic on this occasion set my mind in motion again. Ireland may be just across the water from the UK, but the culture is vastly different in many areas. One such area is that of greeting people. If you enter a shop in England, you would be greeted with, 'good morning, how can I help you?' The answer is easy. You tell the assistant what you want. In Ireland, the greeting is 'how are you?'

I had lived in Ireland for four years but I still didn't know the expected reply. Giving details of your current health status doesn't appear to be the required response. I've even eaves dropped into natives' responses. 'Grand, and yourself' appears to go down well, but the word 'grand' doesn't sound right with an English accent. In the hospital setting, if a nurse greets you with the expression 'how are you?' you don't feel so bad answering the question directly, since the subject comes within her remit.

The outpatients' clinic at the South Tipp contains a corridor with consultation rooms either side. Patients gradually move up along the corridor as the health workers criss cross from side to side. Unlike many men who, in my experience, can only concentrate on one subject at a time, Mr Castineira is omni-aware, taking in all events around him in addition to the one he is concentrating on. Knowing the names of all his patients without looking it up, as each moves to the end of the queue, they are greeted by 'Hello, Mrs XX'. Fortunately, I know the response to this greeting!

Back to the oncology ward, and my blood tests indicated I was still severely neutropenic, although the level had risen slightly. I was reminded to take my temperature regularly, and contact the hospital in the event of a fever. Later in the day, I realised my hair was starting to fall out.

Later that week, I saw Avril at the oncology clinic. She had been losing her hair for about a week, and she was intending to have her head shaved. Avril had not experienced the side effects I had. In fact, it hadn't stopped her walking and swimming routine. Another lady I met, Gillian, did her week's shopping directly after receiving chemotherapy. I could not have done that.

Due to my neutrophil level still being low, there was some doubt as to whether the chemotherapy session would go ahead as planned the following Monday, or whether I would need to wait another week. A decision would be made after the blood test the following Monday. In a week's time, all of my family and friends in Ireland were planning to attend a convention, something we regularly look forward to. It would be an opportunity to associate with others who held the same bible based hope as I do. If I was to receive chemotherapy during that week, it was unlikely I would be able to attend the convention. But if the next session was going to be delayed for a further week, attendance was a possibility, even if for only half the day.

It was the weekend and I had lost about twenty per cent of my hair. Every time I touched it, another handful fell out. I think I was placing more significance on this than other ladies I spoke to. I have always been very fussy about my hair. Being straight and shiny, I have worn it in various bobs for as long as I can remember. The latest bob was the inverted V, short and high at the back and longer at the front, the latest style Anna had learnt. Until I got Anna to cut it short, that is.

Over the years, my friends had teased me about the fact I comb my hair every five minutes. A nice haircut gives me confidence. I had never really been interested in wearing make-up, in fact, my friends had even had to persuade me to wear some on my wedding day. But now a strange thing was happening. I was, at the age of fifty-five, taking an interest in make-up for the first time! Not masses, just a little, but it gave me back a little of the confidence I was currently lacking.

There was another change that was taking place at this time. I had been studying towards a degree in health and social care. Studying part time via distance learning, the modules could be spaced out over a period of up to ten years. OK so it was a bit late in life to be doing this. But I had been involved in this work most of my life and the studies were just consolidating the experience I had already gained.

There were three levels to study, certificate, diploma and degree. I was at the diploma stage. The qualification is made up of modules, some compulsory and several subjects of choice.

The first subject I had chosen was 'mental health and distress'. I had already studied this course and submitted and passed the assignments, although I had not been able to take the exam due to my treatment. I had been waiting to hear from the university to find out whether they would allow me to defer the exam until the following year. (If not, I would have to take the course, including all assignments and exam, all over again.)

My particular interest is advocacy and self-help groups. The next subject I was due to study was 'death, dying and bereavement'. Amongst other things, this course looks into death and bereavement customs amongst the Muslim communities, Sikh communities and in Ireland. This could lead on to bereavement counselling, another area of interest.

However, my recent (and current) experiences were making me think about breast cancer counselling. The university offered a whole range of health related subjects at diploma level, but due to the courses already taken, I could only choose one more module at this level. Should I study the death and dying course, or should I change direction to another subject that had taken my interest lately.

(Note added one year later, June 2008, after rereading the above. 'A year ago, I had not even conceived the idea that, after completing all cancer treatment, I may well not have the energy to do *any* studying.')

Some weeks ago, Mr C had recommended I massage rosa mosqueta oil into my breasts. Rosa mosqueta oil is obtained from the seeds of the rosehip of rosa affines rubiginosa, a wild rose which grows high in the Chilean Andes. Its high concentration of essential fatty acids helps wounds to heal and scars to fade. It would prepare my 'breast' for radiotherapy. I found that rosa mosqueta oil is also a lovely moisturiser. It is however rather expensive when purchased locally.

Since being diagnosed with breast cancer, I had only used soaps and cosmetics made from natural oils like olive oil and coconut oil. I had tried to find cosmetics and soaps containing this rosa mosqueta oil, but nothing was available in the local shops. Surfing the internet I found that rosa mosqueta oil can be obtained far more cheaply, and other cosmetics containing it are also available. Well, I decided that if others can make them then so can I.

The basic ingredients for castile soap is olive oil, (though some soap makers add a little palm oil and coconut oil). My first attempt would be to make castile soap with added rosa mosqueta oil, although I was also interested in other oils reputed to help psoriasis (in case it comes back), such as neem oil, jojoba oil and calendula oil. Esther was also interested in the project so we chose some oils to purchase along with some books on soap making, cosmetics and aromatherapy.

I checked the university website. There was a module on complementary and alternative medicine. I could count this module of study or 'death and dying' towards my diploma, but not both. My daughters would have liked me to ditch the whole 'death and dying' subject. But it is an area in which I could empathise with others. I had found this especially so since my father died when I was twenty five years old. The 'alternative and complementary' medicine is more for my personal interest. Which seemed rather selfish. Monica often said to me that now is 'me' time – there would be plenty of time to think about other people next year when I am better.

It's another irony. Here I am, having had major surgery for breast cancer, facing chemotherapy, my hair is falling out, radiotherapy is just down the line, and then maybe five years of hormone therapy, and what was I worrying about? That the subjects I chose to study in the future would be for my own benefit rather than helping other people! I guess that is why I have always worked in the public sector, hopefully making a contribution to society.

The Irish Cancer Society publish a book on complementary and alternative therapies (CAM). (Another irony CAM not CAT – it is also known as Complementary and Alternative Medicine but always abbreviated to CAM.)[11] I learned a lot from this. Complementary therapies work alongside the conventional therapies (such as surgery, chemotherapy, radiotherapy and hormone treatments).

Complementary therapies focus mainly on psychological needs such as spiritual and emotional (although some focus on physical needs such as fatigue and nausea). Some are not recommended for cancer patients. Hopefully my cancer treatment filled all my physiological needs, but I did feel a need for emotional support. My diagnosis allowed me a little spare time and energy, but not much, so the vastness of different therapies available meant I needed to be choosy.

Complementary therapies include support groups, self-help groups, and creative therapies (such as art, creative writing, dance and music). Previously unbeknown to me, I now realised that my writing my breast cancer experience was for me creative writing therapy. There were also spiritual, meditation, relaxation and exercise therapies.

Some therapies involved praying for a cure or laying on of hands. My spiritual needs are met by my personal beliefs and associations, and I found I needed to take care as some therapies such as some forms of meditation are not in harmony with those beliefs. Although I believe it was not part of God's original purpose for us to suffer sickness and death, I also believe that this is the temporary situation mankind now finds themselves in. Therefore my prayers, rather than asking for a miraculous cure, would involve asking the One who understands my body better than anyone else to direct me to the therapies that would be most beneficial to me at this time. Also to give me the strength to endure.

Other therapies are body-based. Two that particularly interested me were reflexology and aromatherapy. The former is offered to cancer patients through the local support group and I had already registered my interest, though I needed to wait until at least after my second chemotherapy session to receive the therapy. I had already been looking into aromatherapy and planning to make soaps and cosmetics from essential oils as a start.

The other side of CAM is alternative therapies. These are therapies used instead of conventional therapies, such as rigid diets, dietary supplements, and megavitamin diets. The apricot kernel diet which well meaning friends had tried to persuade me to use is one such alternative therapy.

Some of these therapies are viewed as high risk by oncologists who believe there is insufficient research to show they benefit cancer patients. High doses of some vitamins and minerals can even interfere with conventional therapies such as chemotherapy. Of course, a balanced diet is essential for cancer patients. My medical oncologist had advised me not to take any supplements (other than one normal strength multivitamin tablet daily if I wished) during my chemotherapy treatment.

It was Saturday and my hair was falling out in handfuls. The top of my head was fairly bare. I cried a lot that weekend. I definitely would not be able to go out without a hat or wig from that time on. I got out my wig and realised I had made a terrible mistake. There was no way I would have the confidence to wear a shoulder length wig. I needed something short like my new (previous) haircut. Fortunately the wig was unworn and still boxed. I rang Bernie and explained my dilemma. She kindly agreed to exchange it. I arranged to meet her on Monday afternoon.

The following day was another 'coming out'. I had never been seen in a hat before, so I felt self-conscious walking into my bible study meeting on Sunday morning. I arrived late, and sat at the back. Within a few minutes I had burst out crying and walked back out. My friends were very kind.

Next day, I was back at the oncology ward for blood tests. Then Esther drove me to Bernie at Waterford. I chose a wig in a short style, 'shaggy' on top, in a mixture of blonds. The wig was comfortable and looked great with a hat on top. In one way the timing of my chemotherapy was perfect (if I had to have it, that is). It was autumn, and baker boy caps were in fashion. They were available in loads of colours and styles, with bows, flowers and allsorts, and by now, I had bought quite a selection.

Whilst out, I received a call from the oncology nurse. My neutrophil level had risen from 0.3 to 1.2, but this was still not high enough for me to receive chemotherapy the next day. It needed to rise to a minimum of 1.5, so the chemotherapy was postponed until the following week.

Next day, I wore the wig at home. It felt so comfortable I forgot I was wearing it. Which had its down side, as I needed to be careful not to allow it to get too near heat sources!! Most of my hair had fallen out by now, but I was feeling a lot more confident. I now had the choice of wearing my wig, with or without a hat, or a hat with no wig.

It was just a few days before my second session of chemotherapy. Rob had gone out for the day to do a job for his mother. I looked at my hair in the mirror, this was the first time I had viewed the back of my head. Less than five percent of my hair was remaining. What few hairs there were were sticking up all over the place. It reminded me of my granny when she was eighty-five. I was fifty-five.

I got out the hair trimmer and shaved off all the straggly hair on the top of my head. I just left a few strands around the edge. For now, I still had a few hairs that would show around the edge of my hat! I cried extensively. This was my first opportunity to really cry. Rob hates me crying, it has a major effect on his mood. I cannot cry openly with Rob around.

Today I had the space to really let my emotions flow. I was not feeling depressed, just very weepy. Cancer is a roller coaster of emotions.

Sunday was another major 'coming out'. In the afternoon, Rob and I went to the convention. It was an opportunity to associate with around a thousand men, women and children from all over the south east of Ireland who shared my beliefs. I wore my wig for the first time outside the house. It took a lot of courage. My daughters met me by the hotel door and checked me over for any obvious signs of misplaced wig. They said it looked great. Lots of friends made kind comments. Apart from many friends, three of my children were there, four of my grandchildren, my mother-in-law Marie, and the maternal grandparents of two of my children.

My son Leslie is thirty-two, - he was four when we first met and his sister, Yvette, was two. Unusually for those days, their father, Rob, had full 'custody, care and control' (as it was legally defined) of the children from his first marriage. Rob and I were married within a year, and a further year on, Esther arrived. We had to wait another nine years for Anna! Of my four children, only Yvette was missing from this convention. It was good to be there.

Especially as the following week was likely to have its downside.

~~~

Chapter 8

Chemotherapy Cycles 2 - 4

Weeks 25 – 33 (October – December 2007)

Monday morning, it was back to the oncology ward for blood tests. I received a call in the afternoon to say the levels were fine, so it was confirmed that chemotherapy would take place the next day. This time I knew what to expect. Tuesday, the previous month's routine was repeated. It was a little more painful in my hand this time, which pain continued for about twenty-four hours.

However, this time I was also given a prescription to obtain an injection of neulasta and asked to return to the day ward the next day. The neulasta (a growth factor) was to stimulate my bone marrow to increase the white blood cells, prior to them falling around day ten. This would hopefully prevent the severe neutropenia experienced last month. This was needed because I really needed to receive the chemotherapy every three weeks, and not delay it again. I was also given a course of antibiotics to take from day seven to day fourteen, the days when the white blood cell count would be at its lowest.

Whilst receiving the chemo, Lucy arrived for her third session. It was really good to see her. She looked great. If I hadn't known her hair had fallen out, I would never have known she was wearing a wig. It was shoulder length and brown and blond, similar to her own hair. I think the reason it looked so natural was because it was quite fine, whereas all the longer wigs I had seen were much thicker. Also, she still had her eyebrows and eyelashes, and I hoped I would keep mine. As it happened, Lucy didn't stay to have her chemotherapy because she had forgotten to take her Emend capsule, so had to come back later.

After collecting the prescription from the chemist Rob took me home. I wondered how I could possibly attend the hospital the next day, judging by how I had felt last time. But over the next twenty-four hours I felt nothing like as bad as during the first cycle. I felt a bit sick, and slept much more than usual, but I didn't have the abdominal pains I had last time, or the severe nausea. I even got up and did a few jobs.

The injection and antibiotics now formed part of the regular routine, so Wednesday, it was back to the day ward to receive the neulasta subcutaneously (under the skin) in my stomach. My life revolved around my 'week ones', 'week twos' and 'week threes'. My routine and capabilities depended on which week it was. 'Week ones' of each three week cycle now entailed visits to the day ward three days running. Details of treatment received, blood test results and future appointments were all logged in my oncology passport.

The next sessions of chemotherapy followed a similar routine. I stayed in bed most of the time during days one to seven. I felt very tired, sleeping on and off all day and night. My blood pressure was low and I felt dizzy when I got up. I did not feel depressed but lacked interest, hardly even watching any television or listening to music (a subject I am usually passionate about). After several days, the roof of my mouth and tongue felt rough, as if the outer layer of skin was missing. Severe heartburn lasted for about a week, especially pain as the food went down my oesophagus.

Another side effect of chemotherapy I regularly experienced was tingling in my lips and left hand. I usually felt weepy the day after the steroids stopped. During the second week, I started to get up, lie on the couch during the day, and do a few small jobs, but I needed to go to bed early and still slept for several hours during the day. During the third week, I felt a lot better. I wanted to go out, though when I did, I tired very easily. If I over did things, it set me back for several days. In my mind I felt I could accomplish all sorts of things, until I tried to do it.

One 'week three', early on, I was looking forward to going shopping in Waterford with my daughters, (one of my favourite occupations). I had been building it up in my mind, how we would spend the day going round all the stores, having coffee in between, just like we used to. We always shopped until we dropped. And drop I did. After just a few stores. I couldn't move. I sat and waited until Esther brought the car right down to the pedestrian precinct to collect me.

After my third session of chemotherapy, I drank a lot more water every day, about three or four litres. This definitely lessened the side effects. I felt less sick, less dizzy and my blood pressure did not drop so low, though I felt just as tired.

Sadly for me, around this time my youngest daughter Anna left home and moved in with some of the girls she worked with. She was excelling in her hairdressing, and had been moved to another salon at Waterford thirty-five miles away. In some ways it helped us – I was too ill to drive her to and from work each day, and it took the load off Rob. However, I missed her so much. I knew it was on the cards, and completely understood her choice having been there and done that, but deprived of my normal routine of being out and about, it was one more thing to cope with.

During my bad weeks, Rob did the shopping, cooking and most of the clearing up. But men just don't notice untidiness or dusty floors. So throughout my week threes, I caught up on laundry, tidying, dusting, polishing and sweeping. I did just a little each day and had to learn not to worry about untidiness the rest of the time.

During one of my good weeks (after cycle three) I attended an appointment with the nurse at the cancer support centre. She was very supportive, was a great listener and offered me reflexology, counselling and massage sessions subject to the approval of my consultants. Being in Waterford, I decided to call into the oncology day ward there, to see what it was like.

The chemotherapy drug taxol is only administered at Waterford Hospital because some people get a bad reaction and there are oncologists on duty twenty four hours a day there whereas South Tipp oncology ward is open only part time and run solely by nurses. Waterford Hospital also has facilities for oncology patients to stay overnight if necessary. I was shocked by what I saw. The ward was so crowded that the patients' chairs actually touched each other all round the edge of the room. There were arm chairs but not the comfortable day beds like they had at South Tipp. The routine was rigid and there was no sign of any tea and toast. I wished I hadn't gone. (I later learnt this was a temporary arrangement and a new oncology ward has since been built.)

As the treatment progressed, I got more used to the drugs, and side effects lessened (except the heartburn, that was always as bad). But in one way my week threes weren't as good. I was much more tired than during previous cycles. The ongoing chemotherapy was building up. In my mind I wanted to go out and do all sorts but I couldn't physically make it.

It was about this time, during one of my better days, that Esther and I made our first batch of soap. We used olive, palm and coconut oils plus essential oils. The soap itself worked well but our presentation needed working on. However, this prompted us to do more research and we learnt how to produce attractive soaps using a variety of essential oils and other nutrients. We later decided not to use palm oil as its production is not ecologically friendly nor is the oil particularly nutritious for the skin, and we wanted our end product to be nutritionally and ecologically sound.

My next batch of soap was enriched with honey and oatmeal and I learnt how to make attractive heart shaped soaps.

It would be very easy to get carried away when ordering essential oils and other nutrients, but I decided I would experiment developing recipes for just two soaps for the time being, – rosa mosqueta (using rosa mosqueta rosehip seed oil, rose essential oil and ground rosehip for colouring and exfoliation) and honey and oatmeal. I made my soaps during my 'week threes'. As soap takes three to four weeks to cure, each batch was ready by my next 'week three'. Recipes in Appendix 3

Soap making filled multiple needs. It was therapeutic experimenting with the recipes, and producing attractive packaging. It was far better for my skin than the petrol based products I had used previously. I also had some little gifts I

119

could give to health care workers and friends who had been so kind to me over the past few months.

Winter was approaching and I was six months into my treatment for cancer, hopefully half way there. I had only worn the wig that had previously seemed to be oh so important, a few times. It was ok for an hour or two, but after that it irritated, so, instead, when going out, I usually just wore a hat, displaying the few real hairs I still had. But as it got colder, my neck and head felt really cold despite hats and scarves. The wig with a hat on top worked ok, when I could be bothered.

I had been very pleased that my eyebrows and eyelashes hadn't fallen out with my hair. But my boasting was short lived. My eyebrows became very skimpy and one day when I decided to wear some mascara I discovered I had just a few stubby eyelashes. (Towards the end of my chemotherapy sessions, I noticed that all other body hair was also missing). This (the lack of eyelashes!) caused my eyes to be very sensitive to the wind. Even walking across a warm room caused irritation to my eyes. I also noticed a great difference with my eyesight which deteriorated much more rapidly than it normally did.

As the weather became colder, so my skin, face and lips became far more dry and cracked than usual. Rosa mosqueta oil soothed my face, whilst coconut oil helped my lips. I don't really like the smell of rosa mosqueta oil, so I treated myself to some rose essential oil, (which is very expensive) and mixed in a few drops. Rosa mosqueta oil mixed with sweet almond oil (50/50) is also a nice moisturiser for arms and legs.

As the youngest of three girls, I had encouraged my sisters (and daughters) to have their breasts checked. Both sisters attended for mammograms in the UK. These indicated no sign of breast disease. At one of these appointments, my sister Mary was approached by a nurse from the British Cancer Society – she was looking for families to take part in sibling studies. This involved the three of us supplying blood samples and current and past mammograms and ultrasound scans.

My other sister, Anne, was referred to a breast specialist. Whilst her mammogram was clear, the doctor wrote to my breast surgeon requesting exact details of my tumour and the pre-cancerous cell changes.

My oldest daughter's GP agreed to send her for regular checks, although she was just twenty-five. My youngest daughter has not sought any advice to date. Although there were no signs of cancer in my immediate family, my cousin had died of ovarian cancer, and her daughter was diagnosed with stomach and ovarian cancer at the age of forty.

Whilst attending hospital for blood tests prior to the fourth chemo session, I went to see Mary, the breast care nurse, to let her know about the requests for information she would be receiving. When the blood test pack arrived from the UK, the oncology nurse took these blood samples along with my routine pre-chemo blood tests.

The fourth chemo session came and went. My left hand was painful for several days, but as I was getting used to these drugs, the nausea and indigestion lessened. However, this time I was very depressed for about a week. My scheduled four sessions of A/C chemotherapy were complete so I was surprised when the oncology nurse booked me in later in the month (just in case). Perhaps she knew something I didn't. I was scheduled to see the medical oncologist the following week to find out if I would be switching hospitals to receive taxol chemotherapy.

Lucy was about a month ahead of me, so she had already attended for her first sessions of taxol and herceptin at Waterford Hospital. She sent me a text. She was having a bad time, having pains and numbness in her hands and feet, so much so she had obtained strong painkillers from her GP. I wasn't looking forward to taxol.

Whenever I saw Lucy, she made me laugh. Sometimes she gets her words mixed up. She once called Mr C 'Mr Casanova'. Another time, we were talking about our silicone implants, and she referred to hers as her 'prostate'.

"I think you mean prosthesis" I said, "prostate is what men have".

Despite all my treatment, I consider myself very fortunate compared with many of my fellow patients. I met one lady who was unable to control her bladder and wore incontinence pads throughout her chemotherapy and two ladies who experienced severe bleeding from the rectum, necessitating a colonoscopy under general anaesthetic, both of which indignities I have been spared. I also learnt that most breast surgeons in the district are not trained in reconstruction, and I realised how fortunate I was to have a consultant who could carry out reconstruction at the same time as the mastectomies.

My scheduled A/C chemotherapy complete, I attended the oncology clinic. There had been a change in thought since my last appointment with the medical oncologist. Evidently recent studies had indicated that only breast cancers which are HER2 positive benefit from taxol (as well as herceptin). Since I was HER2 negative, I was spared both these drugs. However, he felt I would be better protected by receiving a further two sessions of A/C chemotherapy. It seemed the oncology nurse knew something I didn't when making my next appointment 'just in case'.

Since the side effects from these drugs seemed to be lessening slightly, and following the belief 'better the devil you know than the one you don't' – and remembering what I thought about the oncology ward at Waterford Hospital - this was a welcome alternative. At least I could now work out that my chemotherapy would be completed in January, and radiotherapy completed by the end of March.

I could start planning my life again. Hopefully by next summer I might see the return of some of my energy, and some of my hair. Hopefully, by the summer, I wouldn't need to wear a hat at all. My university exam which I should have taken last October had been rescheduled for the end of April. This was now within the realms of possibility.

I had a few extra days of feeling well, due to the closure of the oncology ward over Christmas. I made some more batches of soap, orange and cinnamon, and another rosa mosqueta recipe using almond oil and coconut oil. This was the first batch of soap which turned out pure white, and was the most successful so far, though a previous batch containing honey and oatmeal was very popular. Anna, who since moving out had discovered the cost of living, whilst visiting for a roast dinner, said

"Mum, have you got any more of that hobnob soap?"

My soap making was just a hobby but Esther was taking hers more seriously. Having researched the dangers in many commercial products, and the benefits of natural oils, she decided to test the market for a skin care business. Even many so-called natural soaps contain fragrance oils which may mimic the fragrance but contain all sorts of chemicals and none of the therapeutic qualities of essential oils. Esther's soaps contained only natural oils with proven beneficial skin cleansing and moisturising qualities, plus other natural ingredients such as seaweed, nettle, honey and oatmeal.

Although some handmade soaps include palm oil, Esther decided not to use this as it contains few nutrients beneficial to the skin and because the rain forest is being destroyed to make way for palm tree plantations, destroying the natural habitat of the orang-utan. Monkeys are Esther's favourite animal.

Although brought up in a meat eating family, Esther has been a vegetarian since she was five, and tried to make her stand even earlier. I can still picture the scene. We were sitting in the kitchen of our Bournemouth home. It was a little before her third birthday. We were eating chicken.

"Mummy, this chicken is lovely. Where does chicken come from?" she asked.

"Chickens" I replied.

"What?"

She made her stand there and then. She no longer wanted to eat meat. I thought she would forget about it, but she continued to protest when I dished up meat, so from the age of five, her diet changed to vegetarian. She has continued this stand to this day.

Esther's home is always filled with wonderful natural fragrances. She makes thirteen varieties of soap, including specialist varieties which some people find helps various skin conditions. She also makes natural lip balms and bath bombs and is experimenting with creams and lotions. She has yet to find anyone who didn't respond favourably to her products.

~~~

Chapter 9

Chemotherapy Cycles 5 and 6

Weeks 34 – 41 (December 2007 – January 2008)

Chemo session number five was due on 25th December, a Tuesday, so was rescheduled for the following Friday. On the Saturday I attended my GP for the post chemo neulasta injection. Sunday morning, I had developed a cough and cold, and by Monday morning, I felt so bad and had a high temperature, I went to my GP to obtain a course of antibiotics. That night, despite taking paracetamol, I couldn't get my temperature to fall below 38.5 C.

Tuesday morning was New Year's day. The oncology ward at the South Tipp was closed, so I rang the oncology ward at Waterford Hospital and was advised to go straight to A and E at South Tipp Hospital. I packed an overnight case just in case, and Rob and I arrived around midday. I was ushered straight through to a nurse, and put into a side room to lie down. Over the next six hours I received two intravenous antibiotics, an ECG and chest x-ray and had a cannula inserted, in addition to the normal obs. Around six in the evening, I learnt they were keeping me in overnight and had found me a bed on the gynae ward.

My high temperature continued for a week, despite two different intravenous antibiotics four times a day. They could not actually find out where the infection was. I was also on IV fluids and oxygen at night. They collected blood from me every day and my blood levels were carefully monitored. They dived quickly.

Antibiotics can cause diarrhoea, and they played havoc with my bowels. Since I had hardly eaten all week, I wondered where all this volume had come from. When I was prescribed a cough mixture, I was told this may cause constipation. The antibiotics and cough mixture battled it out. The antibiotics won.

My consultant was a locum, Dr K from Pakistan I think. He was lovely. I was in a five bed ward. A young lady, Elizabeth who was from Dublin had spent the Christmas holiday with her parents in Tipperary. She was taken ill on the way back to Dublin. She was such a laugh. One evening, she received a scolding from the domestic because she had turned the television round to point towards her bed. She pointed out that the rest of the patients were asleep.

When the domestic left, I asked her, "Are you in trouble Elizabeth?"

I was thinking about words that rhymed with "Tipperary" when the following poem came into my head. I called it *A Limerick from Tipperary.*

Please be especially wary
If you go to the South Tipperary
The nurses* are kind
The doctors* divine

But the cleaners* are ever so scary

*interchangeable according to your experience

Terrible I know! The domestics are responsible for cleaning, and ordering and serving food. One day, a domestic came to get our orders for lunch.

"You *will* have the chicken for lunch won't you", she said.

I replied in the affirmative.

When she asked the next patient, she replied "is there an alternative?" to which the domestic said "well, there's shepherd's pie, but not many people choose it."

Elizabeth ordered the shepherd's pie. I told her she was taking her life into her own hands. When the lunch arrived, Elizabeth realised why not many people chose it, and asked if she could change her mind.

During the first few days I was free to wander around the hospital, attached to my drip stand, so I visited the nurses on the oncology day ward. They arranged for the oncology consultant to visit me when he was attending the hospital on Friday. Friday was a bad day. I woke up feeling sick. The first time I vomited, I was unprepared, and could only find my towel to contain it. I was better prepared the next time. They have very clever large plastic bags. My vomity towel was placed in one, a knot tied, and left in my locker for my next visitor. The whole thing, bag and all, is placed into the washing machine. The bag dissolves during the washing process.

I received a visit from the oncology specialist who warned me that my blood levels were very low. My platelet count was down to 60 (it later fell to 48, the normal range is 150 – 400). He said I would probably have a rough weekend. The strange thing was that, as far as post chemo symptoms were concerned, such as nausea, light-headedness, indigestion and painful swallowing, I wasn't feeling too bad. But so far, I had only been in hospital from day four to day eight since the last chemo. During this period, my blood levels shouldn't yet have fallen, but my white blood cells and platelets were already really low. They still had to cope with the plunge caused by the chemo during days ten to fourteen (since the last chemo).

I did not take my wig to the hospital, just a hat. However, the ward was so warm and my temperature high, I was too hot to wear it. All but one of the other patients were lovely about this. However, one elderly lady kept saying I should put my wig or hat on. I realised she was saying this, not for my comfort, but her own. Well, she didn't have to look at me, did she?

By the next day, I was moved to a private room, put on barrier nursing and told that I should not receive visits from children or anyone with a cold. I was now no longer free to wander round the hospital (but I had a lovely view over the town and surrounding mountains).

Visiting was from two until eight each afternoon, but ministers were allowed to visit at anytime. My minister and his wife came in after their Sunday morning meeting. I heard them scrubbing up, and putting on their aprons and face masks, and I had a good laugh when they came in the room. They lived near the hospital.

"If you need anything at all, just let us know", said Steve.

"And if you fancy something like fish and chips or spring rolls, and it's outside visiting hours, just let me know, and I'll bring it in as your minister."

The nurses were very busy and only came in to administer meds. They knew I was quite happy in there alone. It was a chance to catch up on some writing. Sometimes at night, when less busy, they asked me about my cancer. None had ever seen a breast reconstruction (it was after all a gynae ward!).

"Would you like to have a look?" I asked.

My invitation was never turned down.

Now, Dr K was a locum and not a specialist in chemotherapy. He expressed concern that my blood levels were all over the place.

"Oh that's normal after chemo," I said, "I'll show you."

I got out my oncology passbook, showed him how the blood levels go up and down, and how I have neulasta 24 hours after chemo, to stimulate the bone marrow to raise the blood levels prior to the fall. He had never heard of this so he rang oncology at Waterford Hospital, then prescribed a similar injection, neupogen, for the following two evenings.

Due to axillary clearance of my right arm, all procedures have to be carried out on the left side to avoid triggering lymphoedema. By the time the cannula had been moved three times, some of my veins were refusing to give up their blood.

If you were lucky, your blood was collected by the blood nurse. She always knew exactly where to extract it from. If you were unlucky, it was taken by an intern. They often needed three or four attempts before success. Now I appreciate very much that the consultants were once interns, and I am very grateful for their experience and expertise. And I know these interns have to practice on someone, but did they have to practice on me? I hate it when the needle goes in. I look away, and say "were you successful". Invariably they weren't and had to have another stab.

One evening, an intern was practicing on me. I asked him where he came from. Malaysia. There were quite a few interns from Malaysia, male and female.

"There are lots of young ladies here from Malaysia aren't there?" I said to him during his third attempt.

"Are there?" he replied.

"Don't try to kid me you haven't noticed," I teased.

This inspired me to think up another Limerick, worse than the last.

Down at the South Tipperary
The nationalities vary
Pakistani, Malaysian
Spanish, Croatian
Why can't the world be less wary

Towards the end of my stay, I noticed that my medical notes had been left in my room by mistake. This file, which a year ago hadn't existed, was now several inches thick. I had a quick peek, then put it back. Then I picked it up again and read it from cover to cover.

There were no surprises, but I did copy down the official wording of things that Mr Castineira had said to me in layman's terms. The diagnosis on the right breast was 'infiltrating lobular carcinoma plus lobular carcinoma in situ.' The 'in situ' bit means it hasn't infiltrated the surrounding areas yet. The left breast was described as 'multi centric lobular carcinoma in situ'. In other words they had not infiltrated yet, but there were quite a few of them.

Apparently, Mr Castineira co-ordinated all the reports as all consultants wrote to him. My browsing my file reassured me that he had been very straight with me, telling me everything there was to know. I was right to tell him, back on diagnosis day, that I had confidence in him. Next morning, I told the nurse that my file had been left in the ward.

"I'm not admitting to anything" I said.

She was horrified, not because I'd read it, but because it should never have been taken into an isolation ward in the first place.

Every time any patient or nurse mentioned Mr C, their comment was followed by "isn't he lovely". When he heard I was back in hospital, he called by.

Next day, my consultant said "I hear Mr Castineira came to see you, isn't he lovely?"

"Well, all the women seem to think so" I replied "but you're the first man I've heard say it".

Mr C was transferring to Waterford Hospital, and the nurses were disappointed. New government policy was for there to be just eight cancer centres of excellence throughout the country. Waterford Hospital was one of these but South Tipp was not. Additionally, the breast surgeon at Waterford Regional Hospital was retiring, so there were several vacancies. Mr C was, however, continuing to run an outpatient breast clinic at South Tipperary Hospital once a week.

Towards the end of this hospital stay, I was just lying on my bed waiting to be told I could go home. I was looking at some oranges when another poem popped into my head.

The Little Orange By My Bed

The little orange by my bed
awaits my move its peel to shed,
it needs no plastic outer coating
nor imposed 'best before date' noting.

And as its taste I'm savouring
(please note no artificial flavouring)
my body finds its nutrients bliss
(no added vitamins required for this).

As if I should be further blessed
the room is filled with fragrant zest
which fills my heart and soul with glee
a true aromatherapy.

The peel contributes to compost
for further growth, but without cost.
From one small pip a large tree grew

136

and so the cycle starts anew.

What wisdom's found in the created
a wisdom oft times underrated.
So many needs are simply met
by one small orange by my bed.

(ps, can someone please bring me another one)

After ten days in hospital, since my blood levels had risen sufficiently, I was advised I could go home, though my cough and cold were just as bad as when I had been admitted. I was warned, however, that I may well have the same experience after my next chemotherapy session.

About a month earlier, a friend had asked me if I could type a report for him, as a paid job. I was really pleased about this. I hadn't worked for four years, and was looking for opportunities to alter this. He was supposed to have got the draft to me, but despite reminders, it didn't arrive. I had explained I wouldn't be able to type it the week following chemo, and he had assured me this was no problem. So when I heard I was going home, I sent him a text to say I could type the report the following day. He sent a text back later in the day to say he had given it to someone else.

I burst out crying. I was so disappointed. I had waited for him all those weeks, but he hadn't waited for me. One minute I was feeling strong, the next vulnerable. I was recounting this to Esther, when she asked if I'd like to do the accounts for her business. Would I like to? I had been thinking that, when I am well, I'd like a secretarial, typing, editing, proofreading business and bookkeeping/accounting would fit into this just nicely. I had a little knowledge of bookkeeping, but would need to train further but that was no problem.

In one way, the hospitalisation did me a favour. Most oncology patients I met put on between five and ten kilograms of weight during the course of chemotherapy. This is partly as a result of the steroids that make you very hungry. Whilst I hadn't put on weight during the initial sessions, latterly I had. During the past ten days, I had lost all this weight plus another three kilograms. I now weighed less than when first diagnosed with cancer.

I would have to struggle to find any other benefits of cancer treatment. I suppose I could count the fact that early on in my chemotherapy, I had shaved my legs and under my arms. I have never needed to do so since. My psoriasis continued to be almost clear, just a few small patches on my scalp. (However, the skin on my scalp was very thin, I could feel this when my head was on my pillow. I believe this is due partly to the chemotherapy making the skin thinner, but also due to the psoriasis treatments I had used in the past, which also causes thinning of the skin.)

It's not exactly a benefit, but I have gained a lot of knowledge since my cancer diagnosis. In the UK, I knew the social welfare, educational and medical sectors inside out. Not only had I worked in the sector for years I had also been an advocate for a woman with an intellectual disability for the past twenty years. My experiences over the past nine months had given me a similar insight into these systems here in Ireland.

When I got home from hospital, a friend from Dublin had sent me a book *In Your Face* by Lia Mills.[12] The book was signed by Lia and personally addressed to me. It told her experience of facial cancer. Lia was very open about her emotions. Sometimes down, sometimes jovial. Sometimes she made me laugh, like when she said that the ward smelt of crap and that she hoped it wasn't attributed to her.

The first time I read the book, it was just to read her experience.

I had ordered some new soap moulds, little hearts, and they arrived while I was in hospital. That week, I made two batches of soap, rosa mosqueta and honey and oatmeal, I wanted some presents to give to the nurses who had been so kind. My cough and cold were as bad as when I went into hospital, but without the high temperature. My next chemo session was due a week later. If my cough didn't improve, this was likely to be delayed, which would delay the radiotherapy. I really wanted to get on and finish the treatment so I made an appointment to see my GP.

Prior to the GP appointment, I had arranged a session of reflexology at the cancer support centre. This was my first experience of reflexology. The property had been purchased a few months earlier; last time I had attended the decorators were in. I was surprised at how much work had been carried out since. Downstairs, there were two inviting reception areas, an office, a large art studio, kitchen and toilets. After being offered a cup of coffee and piece of cake, we went upstairs where three bedrooms had been converted into consultation rooms.

The reflexology room was simply but attractively decorated. I lay on a bed, with my head on a pillow. I was covered with several blankets. Soothing music was playing. The reflexologist sat at the end of the bed. She began by massaging my feet with rosemary essential oil in sweet almond oil. Then she worked her way round my feet, concentrating on various points, explaining which body parts they connected to. It was very relaxing. In no time, the hour had passed, and it was time to attend the GP surgery.

There were two trainee GPs in attendance. I had no problem with them being there. Maybe a year ago I wouldn't have wanted anyone intruding into my privacy, but after my experiences of the last year, it really didn't matter if there were two or two hundred people watching. I explained to my GP I had had this cough since two days after my last chemo, and I was due for another session in a week's time. Chances were, if I still had a cough, the chemo would be delayed, having a knock-on effect on the radiotherapy, and I just wanted to get everything out of the way. She prescribed me another course of antibiotics, and an inhaler.

One of the trainees was from Singapore, the other from the United States. The latter explained to me that his partner, Kate, was going through the same thing as me (except her cancer was ductal and mine lobular). Kate was just thirty-one. She had had a bilateral mastectomy, but her reconstruction involved pulling muscles through as well as silicone implants. She was also going to have nipple reconstruction. Being HER2 positive, she had already been through A/C chemotherapy (same as me), taxol (the drug I escaped) and was just finishing herceptin. Like Lucy she had experienced pains in her hands and feet.

My GP noticed from my records that her practice partner had administered my last dose of neulasta. She had never heard of this drug so I explained that this is administered twenty-four hours post chemo to stimulate white blood cell production. The trainee doctor from the United States was familiar with neulasta. He told me this cost 1,500 dollars per injection, and as Kate's insurance wouldn't cover it, they had to pay themselves.

I asked what happens in the United States if someone can't afford medical insurance. He said there is a government provision for medical care but it's very basic, you wouldn't get a comprehensive treatment. He also said that due to Kate's young age, and the probability of there being a genetic link, it would be pretty well impossible to get health insurance in the future. If you are going to get cancer, Ireland is the place to get it.

It was our anniversary (twenty-seven years) and that evening Rob and I, Rob's Mum Marie, Anna, Esther and hubby Dave and children Sam and Ruby all went out for a meal. We had a nice time. On the way home, when I went out into the cold air, I got a coughing fit which lasted a couple of hours. I had six days to get this cough out of the way.

I decided I should stay in for a few days to try to sort out the cough, which is really annoying, as it's supposed to be my good week when I get to go out. I felt quite cheated, as if something I was entitled to had been taken away from me. There really wasn't a 'week three'. There was no 'catch up' time. Outstanding jobs would have to roll over until the next cycle.

My last chemo session was administered by Noreen. Noreen was a multi-skilled staff nurse. She stood in for the oncology nurses when they had a day off, stood in for Mary, the breast care nurse and also worked on the surgical ward and she knew her jobs inside out.

"Do you realise you have seen my treatment all the way through" I said to her "You took me down to theatre for my operation, and you've administered my last chemo session".

However, chemo session six was a bit of a shock. I felt really sick for several days, something I hadn't experienced since the early sessions. To add to this, I completely went off the taste of water, it just tasted like metal, so I wasn't drinking as much, which probably contributed to the nausea.

Next day it was back to South Tipp General for my final neulasta injection.

"Do you know how much this injection costs" I said to Stacia, the oncology nurse.

"It's about 2,000 euros" she replied. "That's about 12,000 euros spent on me just on neulasta" I said.

I was taken aback by Stacia's reply:

"Oh well, you're worth it".

Stacia asked if the neulasta caused my bones to hurt, as some people get this side effect. Fortunately for me, this was another side effect from which I had escaped.

Later in the day I received my appointment for the simulation scan at the Whitfield Cancer Centre in Waterford. This scan takes about an hour and measures up the dosages and direction of the radiation, in preparation for radiotherapy to commence.

This would take place three weeks after my last chemo session. It was really good to have chemotherapy behind me. But I packed a bag for hospital just in case I had a high temperature again.

Due to the infection during the previous cycle, for chemo session six, the oncologist reduced the dose by twenty-five per cent. The regular side effects included numbness in my left hand, tingling in my lips and extreme fatigue for about ten days. The steroids caused extreme hunger, necessitating getting up in the middle of the night for an extra breakfast. This time round, mouth soreness and heartburn were less severe.

On day four, the day after the steroids stop, as usual I felt weepy. Fortunately Rob had gone to his mum's for a few hours so I could cry openly. It was midday and I cried myself off to sleep, my mind full of all sorts of reasons I had to feel sorry for myself. By the time I woke up around five that evening, the reasons had all gone.

I sent Lucy a text. It was a week since her last chemo session but she was feeling really bad with severe pains in her hands and feet. What's more, she had been told they may increase her taxol sessions from four to six. I felt guilty that I had got away with it so lightly.

It was chemo session six, day ten, and I went back to the oncology day ward at South Tipp for blood tests. I chatted to Stacia and gave her some little bars of my homemade soap as presents for the oncology nurses. We talked about how good it was psychologically to know that chemo is over (though I felt a bit guilty, seeing the other ladies receiving theirs!)

143

Stacia explained the future routine. I had an appointment with the oncologist the following week, when he would prescribe me hormone treatment (one pill daily for five years). There would be a follow up visit after my radiotherapy is complete. Thereafter, I would attend the oncology ward every two months for a blood test, seeing the consultant a week later. After this, appointments would alternate with Mr Castineira, seeing each doctor every four months for the next five years.

Stacia also told me I would have a mammogram every year for five years (biannually thereafter). I wondered how this would work since it necessitates squashing the breast very flat, and I couldn't see how this was possible with silicone implant reconstructed breasts which are quite stiff and 'sticky out'. I had another question too. If the lobular carcinomas in situ in both breasts had not been detected by the mammogram, ultrasound or MRI scans, how did we know if I had similar carcinomas in situ in other organs also undetected. I would raise these questions with Mr Castineira next day.

But I didn't get the chance to ask him. The routine at the breast clinic had completely changed. There were none of the familiar nurses in attendance; I didn't even see Mary the breast care nurse. I was shown into a room and introduced to a doctor I had never seen before. He checked my 'breasts', and said everything is progressing fine. He explained that I would return every four months for two years, then every six months for a further three years. I asked if he was also based at Waterford (I like to know what's going on!) He explained that, since Mr Castineira's transfer to Waterford, he had wanted a permanent presence at the South Tipp for the breast patients and he had filled this new position as registrar.

I asked him about the mammograms – he assured me that silicone implants are 'up to the job' being much tougher than their predecessors. He was very nice, answering all my questions unhurriedly, but I wasn't sure if this was the consultation, or a pre-consultation (oftentimes, I was seen by a member of Mr Castineira's team prior to seeing him). As I left the room, Mr C came out of the adjoining room and asked how I was getting on. We had a brief chat in the corridor. I told him I was just starting to plan my life again.

I had been handed over. I wasn't expecting that.

Being thrown off guard by the change in the arrangements, I didn't ask my other question about the carcinoma in situ. This would have to wait another four months. Mr C had always been there giving me the straight facts. I felt some security had been taken away.

The next week is a 'week three'. I was talking to Esther, telling her some of the things I had planned.

"Mum" she said "soon every week will be a 'week three'".

She was right. My 'weeks threes' over the last two chemo sessions had been a letdown. I was very tired.

I made a few enquiries about accounts courses. There was a perfect course during February and March. Unfortunately, this was too soon for me – but at least it showed me I really was planning for my future.

Three weeks after the last chemotherapy session, I had an appointment for a radiotherapy simulation plan, and the radiotherapy was due to start the following week. I also had an appointment (or so I thought) with the medical oncologist that week, and was expecting my hormone therapy to start. I met Cathryn for lunch. She told me how the hormone therapy was affecting her. It had triggered some menopausal symptoms, but wasn't as bad as she had feared. I told her about my experience at the breast clinic. She had already decided to see Mr Castineira on a private basis, to ensure her continuity of care.

Later that week, it was time for the oncology clinic appointment. I was in a side room with Patsy, the nursing assistant, being weighed and having my blood pressure taken, and my file was on the side. I told Patsy I had read my file through whilst an inpatient. This was an ideal opportunity to get an update. But when I tried to read the notes written by the breast clinic registrar, I couldn't read his handwriting!

The medical oncologist was in attendance, but my consultation was with his registrar whom I had also never seen before. After physically examining my 'breasts', he prescribed me hormone therapy, femara, one tablet a day to be taken for five years. I was told to wait another week before starting the therapy. I reminded the doctor I was starting radiotherapy that day, he said that was no problem. It seemed strange to me to start two therapies on the same day, since there were similar possible side effects such as nausea. How would I know which one was causing it?

The femara information sheet warned of possible side effects including menopausal symptoms, nausea (oh no, not again!) and weight gain. I had escaped many menopausal symptoms first time round. Hot flushes hadn't been a problem. I wondered if I would escape them this time.

The oncology registrar also ordered a bone density scan. Bone density is monitored as hormone therapy may cause lessening of bone density – in which case calcium supplements are prescribed. This was my last attendance at the oncology ward for two months. Having attended so regularly for the past five months I realised I would miss the nurses.

Over the weekend I sent Lucy a text. Her chemotherapy was now complete and she was due to start radiotherapy two weeks after me. Hopefully I'll see her there.

~~~

Chapter 10

Radiotherapy Imminent

Week 42 (February 2008)

Radiotherapy involves beaming high doses of x-rays at a tumour or (as in my case) a tumour site after surgery to kill cancer cells just in case any have spread. This is deemed necessary for me because of my tumour's close proximity to my skin, and due to that skin having been retained and used in my breast reconstruction.

Three weeks to the day since my last chemotherapy session, I attended the Whitfield Clinic, a beautiful private hospital in Waterford. It was for the simulation planning scan. We arrived well in time for my nine thirty appointment. Unfortunately, apologised the receptionist, there had been a mix up and a doctor would not be available until the afternoon. However, I saw the unit nurse, Karen, and gained a lot of helpful information. I got out my list of questions. My education continued.

She confirmed there was no reason why I could not start the femara on the same day as radiotherapy treatment. The regular massaging of my 'breasts' with rosa mosqueta oil could continue until the day before my first radiotherapy session. Although my aromatherapy book suggested using chamomile and rose oil over my breast should I develop radio dermatitis (radiation sunburn), she advised against this.

151

Hydrocortisone cream would be prescribed by the clinic in this event.

Other possible side effects include heartburn, a cough and itchy skin. I was expecting twenty-five radiotherapy sessions, however I learned this may possibly increase to thirty. The extra five would concentrate on the scar lines, since this is the most likely area cancer might return.

There is one requirement that really went against the grain. The only soap or cleanser I could use for the duration of the six weeks of treatment was a well-known brand for sensitive skin. It evidently contains no artificial colours or fragrances. I explained to Karen I only use my own hand-made soaps, but as she was unable to ascertain if the ingredients were suitable (I'm sure they would be) she requested I stick to the said soap!

Additionally, I was advised not to use any deodorant on the affected side for six weeks. One of the side effects of femara is excess sweating. Great!! I could, however, make myself some 'talc' and use it on the side to be treated by sifting together one cup of corn flour with two teaspoons of bicarbonate of soda (recipes in appendix 3.6). I was told I would receive more verbal and written information prior to my first appointment the following week.

Five appointments were arranged for the following week then Rob and I went into town for a couple of hours to kill time prior to the actual scan. I reluctantly bought two bars of the said soap. The outer wrapper boasted '..... skincare contains no animal derived ingredients' I read the list of ingredients. The main one was "sodium tallowate" (saponified beef fat) (one of the very reasons I make my own soap. Tallow can cause clogged pores and blackheads and has pretty well no

152

nutritional value to the skin!) (At least there was no SLS!). I later sent an email to the soap company asking them to explain this anomaly.

We were back at the clinic. Stripped to the waist and wearing an open-fronted gown, I lay on my back on the bed of a CT simulator. The purpose of a simulation planning scan is to pinpoint the exact area to be treated. This is called the treatment field. The dose of radiation was also being decided today. My head was tilted to the left and my right arm raised above my head and held in a support to prevent movement. There were two lovely radiation therapists, who explained everything that was going on.

The young Polish doctor introduced himself by his first name (though I can't pronounce it).

"We don't use the word doctor round here" he said.

He prodded me here and there, then drew over the area to outline the treatment field. It was a rectangular shape around my right breast extending from the centre of my chest over to my armpit. I was then inserted in and out of the CT scanner several times. It was noisy as the CT scanner moved around projecting laser beams back and forth over my body. The tilt of the bed was adjusted and the exact treatment field mapped out.

Next I got a surprise. Three small tattoos just above my waist. It stung a bit. (Mustn't tell Anna, she'll want some too.) These would assist in the alignment the following week. The whole procedure took around half an hour, after which, we were free to go. I didn't have the rest of the week off though.

I needed to see my GP to obtain the prescription for femara and arrange transportation to the Whitfield Clinic.

Prior to my first session of radiotherapy I also had my third reflexology session. It was very relaxing. I was entitled to six sessions altogether, the other three would have to wait until after the radiotherapy.

Eileen, the cancer centre co-ordinator, asked if Esther and I would like to give a talk and demonstrate our soaps and other skin care products at one of the monthly breast cancer meetings. We would love to but it would have to wait until the radiotherapy was complete. We fixed the date for the first Wednesday evening in April.

The journey to the cancer clinic is over an hour, up to twice that by the time other patients have been picked up. I am never a good traveller let alone when I don't feel well. My mother in law Marie kindly offered to pay for me to stay in a hotel in Waterford near the cancer treatment centre. I would come home at weekends. I booked the first week then it was off to my GP. I attend a small surgery where there are two GPs, though only one is in attendance at any one time.

After dealing with the hormone therapy (femara) and request for transportation to the Whitfield Clinic, my GP commented on how well she felt I had dealt with the whole ordeal. She said I had always displayed a positive attitude throughout treatment, and although I have in the past on occasions experienced depression, she had seen no evidence of this throughout my cancer treatment period. I agreed. I had only had a handful of days feeling down since my diagnosis nine months earlier. Remaining positive has got me through. I have never believed anything other than that I will recover from my illness and continue to plan ahead for the future. I have always had every intention of being every bit as involved in life as I was pre-diagnosis, if not even more so.

A phone call the next day actually moved me to the point of crying. (Fortunately, Rob was at his mum's again.) Nicky was one of the co-ordinators for the South East Radiotherapy Trust. The radiotherapy unit at the Whitfield Clinic serves the population throughout the whole of south east Ireland. A committee of volunteers had raised funds to acquire three vehicles to transport cancer patients to and from the clinic each day during their treatment period (often around six to eight weeks). They aimed to make the ordeal as comfortable and hassle-free as possible, both for patients and their families, he explained. He offered to arrange for me to be run around in Waterford between the hotel and clinic, which I gratefully accepted. This service is offered at no charge and all co-ordinators and drivers are volunteers. As far as I recall, this is one of the greatest displays of human kindness I have ever come across in my life.

I read the information from the cancer clinic. It said to use a soap with no perfume but didn't specify brands. I decided I was not going to wash myself in beef fat, so I made a batch of soap from almond and coconut oils with no added perfumes. Having poured out one soap to use during radiotherapy, I added rosa mosqueta (rosehip) oil and dried rose petals to the rest of the batch and made some beautiful heart shaped soaps which would serve nicely as gifts for the radiotherapy staff and transport volunteers at the end of my treatment.

Earlier in the week, I glanced in the mirror and saw what looked like a couple of bruises on my head. I didn't remember banging my head, but then again, my platelet count was low. On closer examination, I realised it was my hair starting to grow. It was very short. About a millimetre. But it was hair. I was so pleased it had started to grow back, I kept touching it..

During the weekend prior to my first radiotherapy appointment, I received another call from the South East Radiotherapy Trust. This time it was Elizabeth. She was the co-ordinator for the Dungarvan vehicle. She asked if I would like transportation to the clinic on Monday mornings, and home on Friday afternoons. I lived way off track from their normal route, about fifty miles in fact. I reluctantly declined as my GP had arranged for these journeys by taxi. Later that evening, the taxi driver rang. When I explained exactly where I lived he managed to fit a blasphemy and swear word into the same sentence. I told him not to worry. I would make my own arrangements. I rang Elizabeth back. She was pleased to accommodate me.

Since my cancer diagnosis, various ironies have surfaced. For example, despite this intrusion into my privacy that was thrust upon me unexpectedly and without my consent, I often found myself seeing the humorous side. (This has got me into trouble more than once.) Another irony was that although friendships and relationships usually take months or years to build – I found myself confiding in and trusting people I had only just met. Healthcare workers and patients were suddenly having a major impact on my life.

Arrangements for transportation proved to be another one of those ironies. The one being paid to deliver hospital transport can't be bothered to go out of his way, whereas the volunteers bend over backwards to help, at expense to themselves. They even arranged to take me down as late as possible on Monday afternoons, and back as early as possible on Fridays, to minimise the time I was away from home.

Breast cancer treatment has brought me into contact with so many kind people. I am fully aware that many professionals working within the health service could multiply their income many-fold by working within the private sector in disciplines such as cosmetic surgery. But I just feel very moved that strangers would offer such extraordinary fellow kindness at cost to themselves.

I have met such lovely people here in Ireland who display god-given qualities in their daily lives. It confirms my belief that humans are the product of a creator who gave us his qualities. How could the theory of evolution possibly be true? There is far too much kindness for mankind to be the product of the survival of the fittest. Well, that's my view, anyway.

~~~

Chapter 11

Radiotherapy and Hormone Therapy

Weeks 43 – 48 (February – March 2008)

My first appointment at the radiotherapy cancer clinic lasted about half an hour. Arriving early I went to the restaurant for a cup of coffee. I was surprised to see Cathryn sitting there. Hers was a follow up appointment. Cathryn showed me the ropes, explaining I was entitled to a free cup of coffee after treatment! We went to the clinic together, but didn't get time to chat for long as I was called straight in.

I soon learnt the daily routine. Stripped to the waist, my modesty was preserved by a waist long gown (they even supplied a bag to keep it in). This was kept for the duration of the treatment, taking it home each day. (I washed it each weekend, but judging by what I saw, not everyone did!)

Today was a dummy run. I was not receiving radiation until the next day. I lay on the machine bed. Modesty was discarded. Based on the x-rays taken the week before, this appointment was to check everything lined up. Four small round stickers were placed across my breasts, each marked with an 'X'. I had to try not to remove these for the whole duration of the treatment. This area could only be washed by sprinkling it with water and patting gently dry. Tomorrow it's the real thing.

After the appointment, my transport was waiting to take me to the hotel. Anna had been taking a hair colouring course in Dublin. She called in to see me on her way home.

Still almost totally bald, I continued to wear my hat all the time. I got a few funny stares in the breakfast room. Not many people wear a hat to breakfast. I explained to the staff that I was staying for six weeks and why and we negotiated a good rate. All the staff were lovely. Now that they knew why I was there they fussed over me.

For the rest of the week, I was collected from the hotel at ten thirty each morning and returned by about midday. There was a different volunteer driver each day and all were saints. I soon exhausted my supply of soaps, and determined to bring more the following week.

The cancer centre was busy. There was a constant stream of patients coming and going. Maybe slightly more women than men, but only just. The men mostly being treated for prostate cancer. The women, breast. Every one carried their bag. All the staff were very professional and caring. Despite the heavy traffic, they knew every patient by name.

Each day, the procedure followed a similar pattern. Once called into the radiation suite, I went into one of the two changing rooms, stripped to the waist and donned my cotton gown.

The treatment suite is in two parts, each being a mirror image of the other. Each side had a changing room, an office area with several computers and closed circuit television screens, and the actual treatment room, called the linear accelerator room. Sitting in the office area, radiation therapists can see and hear everything going on in the treatment room. Two radiation therapists work on each side.

There were attractive paintings on the walls and a large pot plant. I didn't know how it looked so healthy since there was no natural light in the suite. When I mentioned this to a radiation therapist, she replied

"What about us then?"

A wide lead-lined corridor, which protects the radiation therapists during treatment, leads to the actual treatment room. The room was much bigger than I had imagined it would be. The machinery is bulky, about twelve feet high. There was a bed protruding from it, and a bulky head that moved around.

There were lots of shelves and cupboards. One shelf housed head guards. A bit like American footballers wear, only covering the whole head. Some poor souls having radiotherapy to their heads must have to wear these and be clamped down to the bed to prevent movement.

I was asked to lie on the bed, with my head tilted to the left. My right arm was raised above my head and secured in two supports to prevent movement. The radiation therapists talked me through everything they did. First we had to get me into position. Then the room was darkened and green laser beams projected from the machinery across the room and my chest. The task was to line the laser beams up exactly with the four Xs on my breasts. I was moved this way and that way. Shoulders brought across, arm nudged up, breast moved over until an exact line up was achieved. The radiation therapists' hands were cold.

Next the difficult bit. Keeping absolutely still, not moving a muscle for maybe five or ten minutes. The lights were turned back on and the radiation therapists exited the room. By the push of a button, the outer door was closed. I had been reassured they could hear and see me all the time. I just had to speak if I was concerned.

Then the actual radiotherapy. The head of the linear accelerator swung over into position to my left. There were clickings and clankings. After a minute or two, a red light went on. This indicated that radiation therapy was in progress. The machine then swung over to the right and the process was repeated. Only my right breast area received radiation, the first burst coming from the left direction, the second from the right. I counted during each burst of radiation. It lasted for around twenty seconds, though I was told this varies depending on the atmospheric pressure.

The computer calculated the dose exactly. The machine head was circular, almost a metre across. There was a square screen in the middle, with lead pins that protracted and retracted so that the radiation was pinpointed to the exact area required. I was told this is the multi leaf collimator that has replaced the previous method necessitating positioning of metal blocks.

It was quite awkward having to stay so still. It made my muscles ache, particularly my right arm. I couldn't relax as I would probably have moved out of alignment.

And that was it. Radiation was complete. Well for today, anyway. The radiation therapists came back, retrieved my arm and lowered the bed so I could get off. I asked about the dose I received. It was two greys per day. I didn't know what that meant, I would have to look it up.

Towards the end of the week, I saw Karen, the unit nurse. She went through a list of questions. She checked my breast. There was no redness or soreness yet. She reminded me I may feel tired and to just give in to my body, only do what I can cope with.

My hormone therapy also started this week. It is a tiny pill. Femara. Cathryn had advised me that taking it at night may minimise side effects. It is an aromatase inhibitor. My breast cancer was oestrogen positive, meaning it relied on oestrogen to grow. In post menopausal women, the main source of oestrogen is from androgens being converted to oestrogen by an enzyme called aromatase. This conversion process is called aromatisation. Femara is a drug that blocks this process thus reducing the levels of oestrogen in the body and hopefully preventing future breast cancer.

After menopause, the oestrogen production from the ovaries reduces to about one third. However, hormones from the ovaries still circulate through the bloodstream and reach the fat cells in a woman's body where they are converted into oestrogens. Therefore women with plenty of fat cells have higher levels of circulating oestrogen after menopause compared to women with less fat cells.[13]

Back home at the weekend, I was surprised I didn't feel more tired. I had used up my bar of soap. I made some more, but when it was time to leave on Monday morning, it was still too soft. Reluctantly, I packed the beef fat!

One day during the second week of radiotherapy, we had 'linear verification'. This was to check that the stickers with the X marks were still in the exact position. Evidently some patients relax after the first week and the stickers have to be repositioned. This was not necessary in my case. Either I never relaxed, or I was relaxed all along!

Another weekly procedure was 'imaging'. The imager, another part of the machine, took pictures of the bones. These were laid over the original images to ensure everything still lined up exactly. This procedure took place after the radiation, so I had to lie still even longer that day.

The visit to Karen, the nurse, was weekly, though patients could ask to see her at any time. She checked for signs of burning. I still didn't have any.

Attending the clinic every day, friendships were soon formed. Everyone was in the same boat. Collette was an older woman. She struck me as being posh. She wore expensive clothes. My first week of treatment coincided with her last week. We had a few coffees together. Living on her own, her diagnosis had made her feel very vulnerable. She made an interesting comment. The staff at the centre made her feel safe. I was looking for that feeling of safety too. It reminded me of how vulnerable I felt when 'handed over' at the breast clinic.

Vulnerability affects people from all sectors of the community. Otherwise capable, confident people become insecure. Treatment is an unknown entity (to the patient but not to the staff). It comes in two guises, psychological and physiological. Some patients need constant reassurance. This is provided to some extent from healthcare workers. But it's other patients who do most of the reassuring.

I only saw Gina a few times then her treatment was finished. She wore attractive patterned bandannas. I had never seen any like them before. She had young children. I don't know how she coped.

I got to know Alex quite well as our treatment overlapped by several weeks. We had a lot in common. We both originated from London, lived twenty or so years in Bournemouth, and she had lived in Ireland just a couple of years longer than me. She was three years older than me. She said she felt ashamed when she was diagnosed. As if it was somehow her fault. I was spared that mental torture.

A tea company was running a competition. Contestants were invited to write a piece about their favourite charity, indicating how it displays extraordinary qualities. 10,000 euros was being donated each month for a year to a chosen charity. Each entry had to be accompanied by twenty coupons from packs of tea. I bought enough tea to last my family about two years. I mentioned the competition to the receptionists and catering staff and some extra coupons came my way.

Since my diagnosis I have come into contact with three cancer charities. Two are support centres, and the third the radiotherapy trust which transports patients to and from their radiotherapy sessions each day. They are all wonderful. I wanted to nominate all three but only had enough coupons for one. I nominated the radiotherapy trust. I wrote my little piece.

This charity had raised funds, through voluntary donations, and purchased three vehicles. They hope to raise more funds to extend the service. The co-ordinators and drivers are all volunteers. Many have full time jobs, offering their services on their day off. They are always cheerful, even though some of the patients are cranky and give them a hard time. I think they are all saints. I sent my entry and coupons off, and messages to all and sundry that I needed more coupons. Nothing ventured, nothing gained!

It was also writing experience. My friend, Theresa, read over some of my poems and stories and said I should enter writing competitions. I entered a story into the Waterford County Council annual writing competition. I have never viewed myself as a writer but Theresa tells me I am one. She's the one who gave me the confidence to take this further. She reminded me about my last job. The job title may have been Careline Supervisor, but didn't I write all the training manuals and training courses, she said.

My studies had been on hold for a year. I was seriously thinking of redirecting these. Health and social care was not now top of the agenda. Maybe I had just had enough of this environment or maybe I was realising that I would never live up to these people all around me. Writing was becoming much more attractive. I checked the website, there was a mini course, starting in May. Writing about Family History. I had already partially researched my father's family. It's a subject I'm passionate about. And an introduction to creative writing. The course would ease me back into studying. I enrolled.

I had already read Lia Mills' *In your face* when I first received it from Theresa.[12] Lia's cancer was facial, and treatment included removing bone from her leg to rebuild her jaw. She had been successful in getting her book published. Now I was reading it again with pen and highlighter in hand. This time I was looking at her style of writing. I made note of her use of short sentences and the present tense. It was effective. I wrote to her to say how much I had benefited from her book.

By the time I went home the following weekend I was more tired. The tiredness was creeping up on me gradually. There were also side effects from the femara. I had been told these should only be temporary. My bones and joints were aching. I needed painkillers to relieve this. This lasted for about two weeks. My stomach was churning over all the time and there were frequent trips to the loo. This also lasted about two weeks. But the most distressing side effect was feeling weepy and depressed. This persisted longer. Should I wait and see, hoping this too will resolve itself. I saw My GP. I decided to take medication, hopefully temporarily, to get me through this.

I rang Cathryn over the weekend. She told me she also had pains in the bones and joints, but this subsided after a few weeks. I asked her about the weepiness. She did get this, but had put it down to worrying about her son. But now she thought about it, it was probably caused by the femara. It had now passed. That was good. Hopefully this would also pass for me.

I spent some time with Esther at the weekend. Sam was talking much more and Ruby was getting about in her walker. Business was progressing. She had bought a new printer and was producing professional looking labels and leaflets. I helped fold them up.   She had boxes of soaps, bath bombs and creams everywhere. She has outgrown the utility room and was relocating to the loft conversion.

I checked her recipe book. There was one for a foot spray, refreshing and deodorising. (It can also be used as an under arm deodorant when I am eventually allowed to use one.)

Witch hazel with a few drops of tea tree and citronella oils. I had all these oils. I made the spray, adding a few drops of lemon oil. I think it was successful. Well, no one has told me otherwise! ^{Recipes at App 3.3 and 3.4}

It was my third week of radiotherapy. Anna asked me to find her a dentist and doctor in Waterford. I sought some recommendations and made the appointments. I went with her. Daughters grow up so fast and become independent. But they still need mum sometimes!

There were coach parties at the hotel that week. I can always tell because there were croissants and danish pastries on the breakfast table. Arriving back at the hotel one day, I got a surprise. My sister Mary and her husband Joe had come over from England for a couple of days. They were booked into the same hotel. I had not seen them for some months. They hired a car so we visited places in Waterford I had never seen before.

I was half way through my treatment and I saw Karen. The doctors had decided I did not need the extra five sessions. I would just be having twenty five. Great. Now I could work out exactly when the treatment would finish. By the end of March normal living could hopefully be resumed.

The daily treatment followed the same pattern. The aching bones and stomach problems were easing. The weepiness was still a problem. I had slight redness over the treatment area, but no soreness. I managed my routine during the week, but by the weekend, I was so exhausted I just crashed out.

Radiotherapy week four. There was a new patient on the Waterford radiotherapy bus, Kitty. She asked me loads of questions. What was it like, how long does it take. I showed her round. She needed constant reassurance. I told her she was entitled to a cup of tea or coffee after each session. We met up in the café after our treatment to await the driver.

It was week five. After this week, there were just two days to go. Wednesday was image day. I had to keep still for twice as long on image day. Next day, they had to do it again. They had exceeded the tolerance level. "You probably took a deep breath just at the crucial time" the radiation therapist told me. I hadn't realised I couldn't breathe!

I was very tired all weekend. The sort of tiredness that doesn't subside even after a good night's sleep. There was a very special meeting on Saturday night and I did not want to miss it. I stayed in bed most of the day to try and shake the tiredness. I really shouldn't have gone out. Half way through the meeting I was feeling ill. We hadn't long left the hall when I was violently sick. I grabbed the hat from my head to use as a receptacle. (It was one of my favourites. Oh well, I would not be needing hats soon!) We made it to Marie's house and stayed there overnight. Despite taking paracetamol, I had a pain through my head that felt like a bolt had been driven through it. I felt the most ill I had felt since the chemotherapy. Radiotherapy was catching up with me. Over the weekend, the headache subsided though the tiredness didn't.

It was Easter weekend. The cancer clinic was closed on Monday. My final two days of radiotherapy were Tuesday and Wednesday. Just one more night at the hotel. I would miss being near Anna. I had seen much more of her over the past few weeks. I was glad to be there because she left home too early. I felt I hadn't finished her upbringing. If it hadn't been for my illness, I could have continued to take her to work each day. She wouldn't have needed to move to Waterford. Not yet. She had grown up so much since she left home. So independent. She'll be OK.

It was my final week of radiotherapy. I was collected in the radiotherapy trust car. There was an envelope for me. One of the drivers had collected a bundle of tea coupons. There were enough to enter the competition again. I was pleased about this. We collected Angela. She was very unwell. It was the last time we would travel together.

Angela had had a row with one of the other patients the previous Friday. Her condition caused severe diarrhoea. She had requested to be dropped home first as it was difficult being away from a toilet for too long. On the way home, another patient complained. He wanted to be taken home first. He told Angela she was a liar. She didn't have diarrhoea. In the waiting room he was watching her and she only went to the toilet once. If he wasn't dropped home first, he refused to use this transport again. As far as I know, he made his own way there after that.

Angela had breast cancer in England ten years earlier. She had breast surgery, chemotherapy and radiotherapy. But although she was prescribed hormone therapy, tamoxifen, she did not take it. Now her cancer had returned in two places. She had been told she had only a few months to live. If I had any doubts about taking my hormone therapy, this certainly corrected them.

In the waiting room, Angela went to the toilet.

"I'm counting" I joked.

Angela didn't have treatment next day so we said 'goodbye'. I will keep in touch with her. I also saw Lucy. Lucy wore her wig all the time. She said it was wearing out. She'd been to the breast clinic. No sign of Mr C. She described her appointment with the new doctor.

"Blessing, prod prod, you're fine, see you in four months, blessing, goodbye."

We decided that Mr Castineira spoilt us. He is such a good consultant, has a great manner and his interest in his patients' welfare goes beyond the call of duty. We expected the same treatment from everyone! Mr C had such a good reputation that the staff at the South Tipp were disappointed when he was transferred to Waterford. The new breast clinic doctor had a hard act to follow.

However, in Waterford, no one had heard of Mr C. He still had his reputation to build here. I was told his predecessor was Mr Watson who had performed breast surgery on many of the women I met. Everyone in Waterford loved him. The South East Radiotherapy Trust, the guys who ran us around, was evidently Mr Watson's baby. It was his idea and he set up the trust. He still ran it. So, down here in Waterford, Mr C had a hard act to follow.

I saw Anna later in the evening. I met her housemates. It was my last night in Waterford.

The final day of radiotherapy had arrived. This was a milestone day for me. Apart from taking a hormone tablet each day for five years, and related scans and follow up appointments, this was the last day of my major cancer treatment. I had stayed at the hotel overnight. I would miss the staff, especially Dana. I gave her a card and some soaps. She was very emotional when we said goodbye. She is from Romania. She said she has got used to seeing me, she didn't have much family in Ireland, and she would miss me. I will miss her too.

My final radiotherapy session had arrived. In the waiting area I talked to a lady I hadn't seen before. She was having treatment to her head. One of those poor souls who had to wear the American footballer helmets. Then Alex arrived. She was half way through her treatment. She was having thirty sessions, the final five being boosters along her scar lines. This is evidently the most likely place a cancer may return. We wondered why I was not being given the booster sessions.

Karen, the nurse, invited me in.

"There's favouritism being shown here' I joked 'some women with breast cancer have an extra five sessions."

Karen explained the reason for this. In the case of a lumpectomy, the scar line is likely to be near the tumour site. If the surgeon was unable to obtain a wide margin, booster sessions are given along the nearby scar line. In my case, the whole breast was removed and my scars are not near the tumour site. I was given radiotherapy because my tumour was near my skin, and this had been well and truly blasted. So I did not need the boosters. I was happy with the explanation.

Karen went through the discharge plan. My treatment field was now quite red and sore, especially round the edge and under my arm. She gave me a tube of hydrocortisone cream to apply twice daily. The effects of radiation would reach

174

their peak in five to ten days' time. After this, the redness should gradually decrease. This may take about a month. I should continue to use the hydrocortisone cream for three weeks after which bio oil should be rubbed over the whole of the treatment field. I still should not use deodorants or perfumed soap, this would need to wait another month.

I was also advised to take Pharmaton, as a temporary multivitamin course. Liquid intake needed to be increased over the following twenty four hours. Six to eight glasses a day is ideal. I was to be on the lookout for fever and contact my doctor in the event of a temperature of 38 degrees or above. It was alright to take paracetamol if needed. Resumption of normal activities should now be aimed for, but taking more rest if I felt tired. Karen gave me a patient discharge instruction sheet, and told me to make an appointment for a month's time.

Karen was lovely. She assured me I could ring her or call in at any time if I was worried. I was then called in for my final radiotherapy. It followed the normal routine. Lie down. Discard gown. Arm over head. Secure in arm rests. Raise bed. Nudge arm. Push shoulders. Move breasts. Cold hands. Laser beams. Call numbers. Lights on. Radiation therapists exit. Linear accelerator head moves. Clicking noises. Buzz. Red light on. Count to nineteen. Red light off. Linear accelerator head moves. Clicking noises. Buzz. Red light on. Count to twenty. Red Light off. Radiation therapists return. Arm relieved from awkward position. Bed lowered. Dismount bed. Return cape. Ten minutes later dignity restored.

The usual 'see you tomorrows' were replaced with 'goodbyes' 'good lucks' 'all the bests' 'thank yous'. I dressed. I remembered to leave my gown and bag in the dirty linen bin. I waited to see the radiotherapy oncologist.

He went through the treatment I had received. Five thousand units of radiation. This was the usual dose he told me. He checked my treatment field and reiterated the need to use hydrocortisone cream. He assured me I was still on their books and could return any time if I was worried. He then told me I had received all the treatment recommended and I had a good prognosis. I liked the sound of that.

I made an appointment for a month later. That was it. It was over. I was free to go. I couldn't though, not quite yet. I had to wait for the driver. So I got a cup of tea and read through the discharge plan. Karen had ticked the boxes that applied to me. All items were as Karen explained. Except the last. This stated:

'Sexual Intercourse. Resume intercourse as directed by your radiation oncologist. Use water-soluble lubricant as needed'.

I didn't recall any one telling me to abstain. I wondered if a radiation oncologist is entitled to direct one to have sex? Isn't this a voluntary occupation? The wording made me smile.

Actually, Karen had not ticked this box. Did this mean I didn't need to abstain in the first place? Or that I'm not to resume? (On a later occasion, Rob joked "better go back and get that box ticked!")

Cathryn had warned me she felt quite emotional on her last few visits to the Radiotherapy clinic. She had made so many friends, she found herself relying on the companionship. She decided on her last few visits, she wouldn't go for coffee, but would gradually wean herself off from the company.

I did the opposite. Immersed myself in companionship until the last.

The final journey home was with Geraldine. She was half way through her radiotherapy. She told me it is good for a cancer to be hormone positive. Since the cancer was caused by hormones, the removal of these through hormone therapy means the cancer is unlikely to return. I had not thought of it this way. I liked this idea.

Arriving home I felt a wonderful freedom. Life could now start again. Well after tomorrow anyway. Tomorrow I had a dexa scan to measure my bone density. The result would be with the medical oncologist by the time I saw him the following week. He would then decide if I would need medication to strengthen my bones.

I wrote to the organiser of the Radiotherapy Trust. Thanked her for everyone's help. She rang me to thank me. I don't think she got many letters. Shame. It's easy to forget how thankful you were when the event is over.

Over the following week, my treatment site became more red and sore. It was leathery round the edge, and particularly painful under my arm where it was peeling. I applied the hydrocortisone cream.

I was tiring easily, but I was feeling good. Either the weepiness had worn off or the meds had kicked in.

A week after the dexa scan, it was back to the oncology clinic. Geraldine was there. She was still attending radiotherapy. She showed me her hair – there was a fine down over her head. She was still awaiting the results of her HER2 test. Most tests give a result of one or three, a clear cut negative or positive. Her result was two. It would take up to six months until she knew her status. A positive would mean a further year attending the oncology clinic three weekly. Lucy still had this to face. I felt lucky to have got away with it.

I was glad to see the medical oncologist himself as I can understand what he says. My dexa scan showed I have osteopenia, a reduction in bone density. As femara is likely to aggravate this further, he prescribed calcium and vitamin D. Weight bearing exercise such as walking would also help.

Back home and I was looking up osteopenia on the internet. It means there is a loss of bone density, but it's not as bad as osteoporosis. Radiotherapy, chemotherapy and lack of exercise can all be contributory factors. Hopefully this could now be reversed.

I had also picked up another brochure at the oncology ward. *Breast radiotherapy: possible side effects.* It discussed long term side effects which could develop in the future. These included: Changes to the colour of breasts. Swelling of the breasts. Shrinking of breasts. Hardening or thickening of breast tissue (I don't think I have any!). Restricted shoulder movement. Damage to the heart muscle (this is only if radiation is of the left breast). Lung problems. Damage to bones (especially the ribs and collar bone). Lymphoedema (swelling) in the arm, especially if lymph nodes in the arm pit were damaged during radiation (once this occurs, I read, it can never be fully cured.) Numbness, pain and weakness in the arm. And the worst one – radiation-induced second cancers, (sarcoma) within the treatment area. Fortunately, this is very rare, the occurrence being about one in a thousand. Should any of these side effects occur (fairly rare), the brochure adds, treatments are available.

I met Cathryn for coffee. She had attended Mr C's private clinic, and been discharged.

It was time for my next breast clinic appointment. Waiting room gossip had it that Mr C's workload had increased since moving to Waterford. He had been told to delegate more, let go a bit. That will go against the grain. His patients regularly see him out in town. He remembers every patient, however long ago, by name. He is always interested to know how they are getting on. That's just his personality – a genuine interest in people's welfare. I can't imagine him 'letting go'.

I was expecting to see the new doctor. I had one question for him. My left 'breast' was often cool whilst the right one was warm. I saw him in the corridor, making the sign of the cross. I wondered why a doctor would do that.

Mary was running the nursing side of things so I asked if she would ask Mr C a question for me, and let me know the answer some time. I was surprised to learn I would be seeing him 'himself'. After examining me, Mr C confirmed the surgery had healed well and the reconstruction successful. He photographed my new boobs. Before and after healing comparison.

My left breast is very slightly squodgy, whilst the right is very firm. He explained that this is due to the radiation, the effect from which can continue on the area for about a year. This also explained the extra warmth on that side.

He also confirmed that I will never again need a mammogram.

He then asked me how I got on wearing a bra. I smiled.

"I don't wear one" I replied. "My husband says I don't need to".

He still had his sense of humour.

"It's the only benefit I can think of from having breast cancer", I continued.

My new boobs might not be made of the right stuff, but at least they are in the right place.

Since Mr C no longer performs surgery at South Tipp Hospital, he is not now followed by his entourage at his breast clinics. But back in the days when he was, and my brain was more active than my body, the following poem had popped into my head.

The Consultation

I lie on the bed
stripped to the waist
but my dignity is preserved
twofold.
By the curtain drawn
around my bed
and the cloth I am given
to cover my breasts.

I lie all alone
dignity thus preserved.

The door is opening.
I hear the shuffling
of a hundred and one pairs of feet.
The curtain is pulled back
to reveal
the consultant
and behind him
a hundred pairs of eyes.

The cloth is removed
to reveal my breasts.

Two hundred and two eyes
peer at my breasts.
Two hundred and two hands
feel my breasts.
One hundred and one mouths
discuss my breasts.

The cloth is replaced
the curtain is closed.
One hundred and one pairs of feet
shuffle out the door.

My dignity is restored.

Today, I left that appointment feeling reassured

~~~

Chapter 12

Coping Strategies

Early on in my cancer treatment, after surgery but before chemotherapy, I spoke to my friend Doreen in England. She had come through breast cancer successfully seven years earlier. Unknown to me, I still had the most difficult part of my treatment to face. Having been there, she had more insight. She asked me an interesting question.

"What are your coping strategies?"

One of hers was to make sure she accomplished something worthwhile every day. Then at the end of the day she could say,

"Today I rang a friend, went shopping, went to church or visited a neighbour. I have achieved something today".

I had no such strategies. Well, not planned ones anyway. I had not even conceived the idea of having coping strategies. There were days when I could accomplish nothing. Not even listen to music. My body was so tired, I could only sleep. I listened to my body. I gave in to it. If it demanded rest, I gave it rest. If it allowed activity, I enjoyed it while I could.

There were other days when I accomplished a lot. Not in comparison with when I am well. But a lot for being ill. Some housework, phone calls, even shopping. Rob was very understanding. If I stayed in bed, he brought me my meals. If

I was busy in the kitchen, he would say "you must be feeling a bit better today". Sometimes, I would think I could accomplish a simple task such as loading the dishwasher, to find I had to stop half way through.

That question – what were my coping strategies - is a question I can now answer in hindsight. There were five major strategies, and several mini ones too.

My spirituality was a major coping strategy, but looking back, I could have made it more so. Any deficiency is on my part, not my creator's. I believe he originally designed the human body perfectly. Although sickness was not part of his plan for us, he informs us why it is part of life at this time. He assures us that a problem-free life on earth will soon be possible. He gives the advice we need to cope with life's problems now plus a channel of communication available 24x7. At times I allowed the busy-ness of breast cancer treatment to distract me, thus depriving myself of the foremost coping strategy.

A major coping strategy was keeping myself informed. I researched every aspect of my diagnosis and treatment. I questioned doctors, nurses, physiotherapists, radiation therapists, receptionists. I read books, researched the internet, attended cancer support centres and talked to other patients. Every new word I heard, I looked up. As questions entered my mind, I wrote them in my diary and asked at the next consultation. If the next consultation was too far away, I rang Mary, the breast care nurse. I wanted to know everything about every aspect of my treatment. I've learnt a lot.

When attending for appointments at hospital, I sought other patients who wanted to talk. I exchanged experiences with dozens of women. But not all patients find this a coping strategy. Not everyone wanted to exchange information. Even aside from the privacy angle, some people did not even want to know about their own treatment. Sometimes, I would ask a fellow patient which chemotherapy drugs they had received. They didn't know. I couldn't have coped with that. But we are all different.

I was particularly keen to learn how I could help myself. Suzannah Olivier's book taught me the optimum diet to cope with my illness and treatment and promote recovery. I believe I further assisted my body to cope by removing contact with as many chemicals and artificial additives as possible from skincare, cosmetic and household products. I informed myself about all complementary therapies available and chose those appropriate to me. By applying this knowledge I felt I was doing all I could to work along with the consultants for the best possible prognosis.

My next major coping strategy was one I didn't even know I was experiencing. That of 'writing therapy'. From my very first hospital appointment, as soon as I got home, I wrote down the whole experience. Where I went and why. Who I saw. What they said. What I said. How I felt.

I found this benefited me in at least two ways. Writing each experience after the event, together with my feelings, made the matter feel 'dealt with'. As if I had shared it with someone. Unloaded my burden. I could now move on to the next stage.

It also helped later. Of all the treatments I received, I felt my lowest during the week following each chemotherapy session. When expressing this to Esther, she suggested I re-read my accounts of previous sessions. It worked. I had felt just as bad last time. But it was only temporary. This reassured me that within a week or two, I would be feeling better.

Checking out some web sites, I came across the thought that therapeutic writing (described in the report as an informal, safe and personal process of putting thoughts and feelings into word) can be a psychotherapeutic tool. The report continued that this is based on the belief that recording memories, fears, concerns and/or problems can help relieve stress, promote health and well-being.[14]

Further I came across another news report suggesting that encouraging cancer patients to write down their deepest fears about the disease may improve their quality of life and ease stress.[15]

Major coping strategy number four was one that Mr C planted the seed for way back at the first appointment. He told me my prognosis could, to some extent, depend on my having a positive attitude. I needed to believe I was going to get better. I needed to think about the future, imagining myself there and planning what I was going to do. I found that relaying these thoughts to family, friends and other patients kept me positive. Sometimes I have been overly optimistic, but if that is what helped me make it, it didn't do me any harm.

My final major coping strategy has to be humour. Seeing the funny side of things whenever I could. This is a reflection of my normal life. I find things funny when others don't! It sometimes gets me into trouble. Of course there were many incidents that were positively not humorous. I found nothing funny about lying in bed after chemotherapy, wanting to go to sleep and not wake up. But I couldn't help but laugh at the following scenario. There I was, bald as a coot, skin a horrible yellowy colour, and I decided to apply some mascara to make myself more beautiful. When I eventually found the stuff, I discovered I had no eyelashes anyway!

One day Rob and I were at our GP Paddy's surgery – the appointment was for Rob on this occasion. They were discussing a medical procedure when I piped in with

"Oh, he's just jealous of my silicone implants. He wants some plastic parts as well."

Fortunately, Paddy also has a good sense of humour.

Which brings me on to the mini coping strategies.

Although I felt too tired to go out most of the time, I grabbed every good day or moment to do things I enjoy. For me, these included simple things like seeing my grandchildren or being taken out for a coffee. This put some normality into my abnormal life. But I tried not to be disappointed when I couldn't make it.

I tried out a few hobbies. During the chemotherapy period (well for the first four sessions) I looked forward to making soap during my 'week threes'. I found this very therapeutic and creative. Anything creative would have worked such as calligraphy, art or sewing.

Although I was too exhausted to do much physically over the course of my treatment it was still important for me to feel useful. Even just to accomplish something simple like making someone a cup of tea.

There were many opportunities to encourage other patients, you can really empathise when you are going through the same thing. Some other patients were glad to share experiences. Some were pleased to find someone willing to answer questions or just listen. I believe the majority of psychological support is with fellow patients. It goes both ways of course. Sometimes we take, sometimes we give.

When friends visited me at home, I was not too proud to ask for help. Maybe the pillowcases needed changing, or the bathroom sink needed a clean. Jobs that are normally accomplished in a few minutes but are too much when you are sick. Friends are always pleased to complete such tasks and I felt much better knowing they were done.

A coping strategy I learnt was not to feel I had to chat to people if I wasn't up to it. One visitor in hospital wanted me to join in deep conversations. I felt I had to chat to entertain her. I was exhausted when she left. After that experience, if I was too tired to talk, I said so.

Finally, it helped having something to look forward to long term. When Esther asked me to help in the administrative part of her business, it gave me something to plan for. And it felt good that someone else was confident that I would recover.

~~~

Chapter 13

Getting my Life Back

Week 49 on

Rob and I were still living in the garage. We needed to do something about this. I rang our engineer Derek. We would have to apply for planning permission in two stages. First to apply for retention of change of use from garage to living accommodation. Secondly to extend the building. Two lots of application forms. Two lots of maps. Two lots of fees.

Our engineer believed our application was more likely to be successful if we applied to demolish the old cottage. Several years ago, a local authority planning officer had said the best thing we could do was knock down the cottage and start again. We reluctantly incorporated this into our latest application. (We later had the application granted by the local council subject to the cottage being conserved!)

I needed to free Rob from domestic duties so he could concentrate on the house plans and getting the site ready. Cooking duties recommenced. I found I needed a little sleep each afternoon.

The 'house' had not really had a good clean for some months. During chemotherapy, I used to have a clean through during my 'week threes'. I was disgusted with myself for leaving it so long. But during the last two sessions, I was too ill to do even that. And I had been tired ever since. It had been three months. Dusting and vacuuming my bedroom were spread out over a period of three days. Next day I swept and washed the kitchen floor. The main room took a couple more days. All this used to be accomplished in a few hours.

Esther's business was increasing. I helped her when I could. The week after radiotherapy finished, Esther gave her presentation at the cancer support centre. It was one of the Wednesday evening meetings for breast cancer patients and ex patients. Esther explained why she looked into making soap in the first place. When I was diagnosed with breast cancer, she had researched ways of removing additives from her diet and cosmetics. Initially, it was just for her family but then people wanted to buy it from her.

She registered a company in Ireland, Naked Soap Co, making and selling products from natural ingredients with no artificial additives. Her range includes soaps, lip balms, Dead Sea bath salts and bath bombs. She also sells essential oils and rosehip oil (rosa mosqueta) and made a cheeky comment that I use it to smooth away my wrinkles. The presentation went down well and there was a lot of interest in her products.[Appx 3.9]

Informal chat followed. A young lady had undergone mastectomy but not reconstruction. I asked if she would like to see my reconstruction. She did. We found a quiet corner. She was amazed. Then I chatted to a lady who had her mastectomy and reconstruction five years ago. She had had the effect of nipples tattooed onto her reconstructed breasts. She offered to show me. I could not believe what I saw. It looked so real. The effect of the areola, then a darker circle where the nipple would be. It looked so three dimensional. It is very clever.

She was given a tube of anaesthetic cream to apply before each session (there were two sessions as the first tattoo was fairly feint, and the second darkened the effect.) She had felt a little pain but put that down to not applying enough cream. I still had no feeling in the area anyway. I previously thought I would not bother with nipple tattoos, but now I am not so sure.

Almost a year on from surgery, I still had little feeling under my right arm. I had slightly more feeling around the edge of my 'breasts', but none over most of the surface. However, I sometimes experienced an itch. Scratching where I thought it was didn't work. There was no relationship between where the itch was and where I thought it was! In fact, the itch appeared to be somewhere in the middle of the silicone. I have heard that amputees still get feeling in their limb. I suppose it is the same with amputated breasts!

Having reconstructed breasts (and the non-necessity of wearing a bra) has both removed from and added to family entertainment. Rob is now deprived of one of his former favourite past-times – removing my bra without my knowledge. And there are plenty of jokes. When the children were young, we differentiated between breast feeding and bottle feeding with the expressions 'booby' and 'plastic booby'. 'Plastic booby' has now taken on a new meaning.

Sadly, for over a year I have been unable to participate in my favourite sport – swimming. I have a small swimming pool in the garden. I usually clean it out late spring each year, then maintain the chemical levels during summer. May last year was especially hot, so I cleaned it out early. I only used it once, and but then received my diagnosis. I have been unable to use it since (not because of the illness – but rather because of the treatment!) This summer is going to be better.

Wandering around my garden one day, I came across a pile of plant pots and canes. Prior to my tiredness over the past few years, I had grown much of our salad and vegetables. (We also used to produce our own eggs, milk and honey amongst other things.) I had forgotten all about it until I saw those pots. I wanted to resume this activity, and I had the strength to do just a little.

There was an obstacle. We live on a mountainside, surrounded by sheep farms. We have two ponies and three pet sheep on our own six acres. (EU legislation requires us to have a flock number for our three pet sheep. I am officially a shepherdess!) The original sheep were orphaned lambs from neighbouring farms. I reared them by bottle feeding them (plastic booby!). They are very tame, coming right up to us to be stroked (even the lamb born on our farm this year). (Much to Rob's annoyance, I refuse to eat home produced meat, on the principle that I don't eat my friends!)

But they nibble everything, including flowers and vegetables. Problem is how to prevent them eating my vegetables. The garage/barn/house is still surrounded by scaffolding (whilst awaiting the second planning permission). Rob carried the pots and compost up to the scaffolding planks, where I now have a flourishing vegetable garden.

I am also engaging in a new activity – well one I haven't done for twenty-seven years. And I didn't do much of it then. Now that our family of six is reduced to two, Rob decided he would like to return to motor biking, one of his former loves. He bought a vintage BMW. I have been on it several times, and amazed myself that I really enjoy it (another thing I'm glad my mother is not aware of!)

Around this time I also made my first major journey for a year, (but not on the bike – that's for short journeys for now). Up until now I would have felt too sick to make a long journey. We went to see our granddaughter Oceana in her first ballet performance at Dublin. She's four.

My cancer diagnosis has changed my outlook on life. It has taught me what is really important in life, and what is not. I don't worry about things like I used to. I just live each day as it comes. I'm far more content with life. I just do what I can – and don't worry about what I can't. Perhaps I should have received my diagnosis thirty years ago!

~~~

Chapter 14

I *am* a survivor

Week 52

It's a year to the day since my first appointment. It's the first Wednesday in May, and like last year, it's as hot as midsummer. I've had a clear month since my radiotherapy ended. I'm gradually getting some strength back, but I still have some way to go. Today is a busy day. I have two arrangements, both at the same place. I don't usually do two things in the same day, so I will probably have to stay in tomorrow.

My morning appointment at the cancer support centre is my sixth session of reflexology and it's very relaxing. The lady to follow is in the midst of chemotherapy. I feel sorry for her. I was originally entitled to six sessions, but I can increase this to nine if I wish. However, I decide to make this my last appointment. Oh, I love it, but I am feeling so much better. There are other pour souls who need it much more than I do. I can always use the other three sessions in the future if I need to.

On the evening of the first Wednesday of each month there is a meeting especially for breast cancer patients and survivors. I take it I fit into the latter category. Spotting my short hair (thick grey curls had replaced my former straight brown hair), a newcomer asked me how long after chemotherapy was completed it had started to grow. She had just two sessions left. She then asked me about the whole radiotherapy episode. Having explained the procedure, I told her that compared to chemotherapy, it's like going on holiday. (This is, however, not everyone's experience. Some women sail through the chemotherapy, but find the radiotherapy harder to cope with.)

I love this meeting. It is great to share experiences and support. It goes both ways – encouraging others who are in the midst of their treatment and receiving support from those who have already been there. Where else would you find a group of women willing to display their scars, breast implants and nipple tattoos?

I met Margaret for the first time. She had undergone surgery, chemotherapy and radiotherapy exactly two years before me. The first summer following her treatment, she thought how much better she felt than the previous year. However, the following summer she had even more energy, it was an ongoing process. I have that to look forward to.

Over the past year I have benefited greatly from literature produced by the Irish Cancer Society. Tonight we have a talk about 'Reach to Recovery', a scheme in which volunteer breast cancer survivors are trained to support current breast cancer patients. When the diagnosis is given, patients are asked if they would like to be put in touch with someone who has gone through the same experience. This lady is currently the only trained volunteer in the area.

I am the only person present to register an interest. But it turns out I don't qualify anyway. I am told that three years have to elapse before a volunteer can be trained. Evidently, a breast cancer patient is not considered 'cured' until she has survived three years since surgery. 'Reach to Recovery' volunteers encourage new patients because they are survivors. I understand their reasoning but it wasn't the most tactful talk I've heard considering the audience.

I will have to find another avenue to offer support.

And if anyone thinks I am going to spend the next two years worrying about a breast cancer recurrence, they have another think coming. Of course, I'll follow all medical advice and I'll be there for anyone I can help. But as for letting another two years elapse before I consider myself a survivor, no way! I *am* a survivor. And my life gets back on track from today. Normal activities resume from today. Maybe at a slower and more spread out pace for now, but at least I am heading in the right direction. There will be swimming, walking, art classes, training courses, family history, writing, motor biking, jobs to complete, grandchildren to take out, meals out with daughters, charity work. I don't have enough time for negative thoughts about cancer returning. It's 'goodbye breast cancer.' I am far too busy to worry about you. I have a life to get on with.

~~~

Appendix 1 - Time Table

	1st Week	2nd Week	3rd Week	4th Week
May	Mammogram	Ultrasound	Dermatologist	Needle Core Biopsy
June	Diagnosis	MRI Scan	Radioactive Injections & Surgery 1	Mastectomies Reconstruction Inpatient
July	Inpatient	Wound Care Nurse	Wound Care Nurse	Wound Care Nurse
Aug	Wound Care Nurse	Wound Care Nurse	Wound Care Nurse	Wound Care Nurse
Sept	Wound Care Nurse	Wound Care Nurse	Chemo 1	Blood Tests
Oct	Hair Falls Out	Blood Tests	Chemo 2	Blood Tests

Nov	Blood Tests	Chemo 3	Blood Tests	Blood Tests
Dec	Chemo 4	Blood Tests	Blood Tests	Chemo 5
Jan	Infection Inpatient	Infection Inpatient	Chemo 6	
Feb		Simulation Planning Scan	Radiotherapy Daily	Radiotherapy Daily
March	Radiotherapy Daily	Radiotherapy Daily	Radiotherapy Daily	
April			Radiation Oncologist	
May	Cancer Support Meeting			

Appendix 2 - Glossary

Adriamycin (also called doxorubin)
A chemotherapy drug used in breast cancer

Alternative Medicine (Therapy)
Treatment by means other than conventional medicine

Anti-Emetic
Medication to prevent nausea and vomiting

Aromatase
An enzyme which converts androgens to oestrogens

Aromatase inhibitor
A drug which inhibits aromatase

Axillary dissection
Removal of most or all axillary nodes (under the arm)

Bilateral
Both sides

Bilateral risk-reducing mastectomy (also known as bilateral prophylactic mastectomy)
The surgical removal of both breasts when no cancer is currently present to help reduce the risk of developing it in the future

Biopsy
Removal of tissue from the body to ascertain if cancer cells are present.

CAM
Complementary and Alternative Medicine

Cannula
A tube inserted into a vein through which drugs are administered

Chemotherapy
Treatment of a disease by chemicals (drugs) which destroy cancer cells

Contralateral mastectomy
When cancer has developed in only one breast, but the other breast is also removed as a risk reducing strategy

Conventional Medicine
Treatment by conventional methods such as surgery, radiotherapy, chemotherapy

Colonoscopy
Examination of colon by inserting camera

Cyclophosphamide
A chemotherapy drug used in breast cancer

Cytotoxic
Chemicals that are directly toxic to cells, preventing their reproduction or growth.

Dexa scan
A scan which measures bone density

Essential Oil
An oil derived from plants usually by distillation but sometimes by pressing (as in the case of citrus oils)

Hormone Therapy
A daily pill to reduce the level of a hormone (such as oestrogen) in the body

Invasive lobular Carcinoma
Infiltrating cancer of the breast lobule

Invasive Ductal Carcinoma
Infiltrating cancer of the breast duct

Leucocytes
White blood cell

Linear Accelerator
External beam radiotherapy machine

Lumpectomy
Surgery to remove a lump from the breast

Lymph Nodes (glands)
Small glands in the lymph system

Lymphoedema
Swelling caused by fluid retention due to obstruction in lymph drainage system

Mammogram
X-ray of the breast to detect the presence of cancer

Mastectomy
Surgery to remove the breast

Methotrexatel
A chemotherapy drug sometimes used in breast cancer, also used to treat psoriasis

Multi leaf collimator
A part of the accelerator linear machine which ensures radiation targeted at correct place

Needle core biopsy
Removal **of** samples of breast tissue from various locations in different directions from a single surface area for further examination

Neulasta
A growth factor that stimulates bone marrow to increase production of white blood cells

Neutropenia
Decrease in white blood cells (mainly neutrophils)

Neutrophil
A white blood cell

Oncologist
Cancer specialist (the medical oncologist deals with chemotherapy whereas the radiation oncologist deals with radiotherapy)

Osteopenia
A reduction in bone density

Osteoporosis
A reduction of bone mass which may lead to fractures

Radiotherapy
The treatment of disease by radiation

Rosa Mosqueta
A carrier oil obtained from pressing rosehip seeds from the plant rosa rubiginosa

Sentinel lymph node biopsy
Removal of several nodes (or glands) from under the arm to test for cancer cells

Simulation planning scan
A scan to measure and pinpoint the exact area to receive the radiotherapy

Subcutaneously
Under the skin

Sodium tallowate
Soap made from beef fat

Saponification
Process of converting oils to soap using sodium hydroxide or potassium hydroxide

Ultrasound
Obtaining an image using high frequency sound waves

Phototherapy
Treatment using light (UVB and UVA used for psoriasis)

Wide margin lumpectomy
Surgery to remove a lump from the breast, including a margin
of healthy cells

Appendix 3
Recipes for Skin Care Products

Important – Everyone, especially those with allergies or a medical condition, should check the suitability of using essential oils. If in doubt, seek qualified advice.

People with cancer, other medical conditions or who are pregnant, should seek advice from a medical doctor before using essential oils. People with oestrogen dependant cancer should avoid citronella, lemon eucalyptus and lemongrass oils. Neroli or petitgrain may be suitable alternatives. Avoid citronella, lavender, rosemary, peppermint and rose during pregnancy. This is not an exhaustive list of cautions.

Essential oils are very concentrated and are used in very small quantities such as one drop. They should never be used directly on the skin but always diluted in a carrier oil such as sweet almond oil.

3.1 Handmade Soap

Health and Safety

Caution Sodium hydroxide can cause burns. Never make soap or leave equipment in the reach of children or pets. Wear long sleeves, rubber gloves and goggles. If any splashes of lye or soap mixture touch the skin, wash off immediately with plenty of cold water. Ensure there is plenty of fresh air. Do not inhale fumes from lye. All measurements are by weight, even the liquids.

Equipment you will need, a large stainless steel pan (never use aluminium). Two wooden spoons, a pyrex jug, a silicone spatula, a cooking thermometer, a pyrex or ceramic bowl. A hand blender is also useful. Mould(s). Each recipe makes approx 2 pounds weight of soap. Suitable moulds are wood, pyrex, silicone or plastic. I find a two-pound pyrex loaf tin is the ideal shape. Alternatively I use 16 individual heart shaped chocolate moulds, each soap weighs approx 2 ounces.

3.1.a Basic soap making recipe

Oils - Pour oils into the stainless steel pan and heat gently until the coconut oil (and beeswax if using it) have melted. Set aside until the oils are approximately 100 degrees F. Mix thoroughly with a wooden spoon.

Lye - Pour water in the pyrex or ceramic bowl. Very carefully add the sodium hydroxide, mix with a wooden spoon until dissolved. (This mixture is the lye.) Do not inhale the fumes. This will quickly rise in temperature. Leave to cool to 100 degrees F.

Grease the moulds with a thin layer of oil. Prepare any nutrients.

Carefully pour the lye into the oils. Mix well (a hand blender on slowest setting is useful), until the mixture reaches 'trace'. You have reached 'trace' when the blender or wooden spoon leaves a feint trace or mark on the top of the mixture. (Don't keep mixing until it has the consistency of custard, as it will be too difficult to pour into the moulds.) Add nutrients. Mix well, pour into moulds. Set aside for 24 – 48 hours. Remove from moulds. If using a loaf tin, slice at this time. Leave to mature for a month. (When using individual moulds, after the 24 hour period, I put my moulds in the freezer for a few hours. This helps them pop out of the mould easily.)

3.1.b Rosa Mosqueta soap bar

Oils -   16 oz almond oil
          8 oz coconut oil
Lye -   9 oz water
          3.75 oz caustic soda
Nutrients – 0.75 oz rosehip oil
          Few drops of rose oil
          Pinch rosehip powder or large pinch dried rose petals
          (optional)

Makes 16 x 2 oz hearts or 1 x 2lb loaf tin

3.1.c Honey and Oatmeal soap bar

Oils-   8 oz olive oil
              8 oz sunflower oil
              8 oz coconut oil
              1.75 oz beeswax
Lye -   9.75 oz water
              2.75 oz caustic soda
Nutrients   1.5 oz ground oatmeal
              1.5 oz honey
              1.25 oz wheat germ or sweet almond oil

3.1.d Pure White Perfumeless soap bar (for sensitive skin)

Oils -   16 oz almond oil
                8 oz coconut oil
Lye -   9 oz water
                3.75 oz caustic soda

3.1.e Pure Castile soap bar

Oil -   16 oz pure olive oil
Lye –   6 oz water
                2 oz caustic soda

3.1.f Deodorising soap bar

Oil -   16 oz pure olive oil
Lye –   6 oz water
                2 oz caustic soda
Nutrients   Ti Tree essential oil (few drops)
                Lemongrass or Citronella Essential Oil
                (few drops)

3.2   Facial moisturiser

Massage neat rosa mosqueta rosehip oil into face or use
mixture 50% rosa mosqueta oil and 50% sweet almond oil.

3.3.a. Deodorant (underarm)

Into 100 ml witch hazel, add 2 drops ti tree oil and 5 drops citronella or lemongrass essential oil. Shake well before use

3.3.b. Deodorant powder

Dip a damp flannel into a pot of baking soda. Apply to under arms.

3.4 Foot spritzer

As deodorant above. A few drops of any of the following essential oils may be used instead. All have deodorising properties:

Petitgrain
Rosewood
Neroli
Bergamot
Cypress
Lemon Eucalyptus
Lavender
Rose Geranium

3.5.a Lip Balm

Mix together 1 teaspoon coconut oil, 1 teaspoon almond oil and half a teaspoon grated beeswax. Melt over a low heat until the beeswax has melted. Mix

thoroughly and leave to cool.   Place in small clean
container.

Alternatively add one drop of your favourite essential
oil.

3.5.b   Lip Moisturiser Gloss

Massage a little coconut oil into the lips

3.6   Talc

3.6.a   To one cup of corn flour add 3 drops of your favourite
essential oil. Place in a sealed jar and shake well.

3.6.b   To one cup of corn flour add 2 teaspoons bicarbonate
of soda (bread soda).   Place in sealed jar and shake
well.

3.7   Tooth powder

Dip a damp toothbrush into a small pot of sodium
bicarbonate (bread soda).

Alternatively, add two drops of peppermint oil to half
a cup sodium bicarbonate.   Mix thoroughly and put in
a lidded pot.

3.8   Hair Gel

Dampen hair and apply Aloe Vera gel (the purest I have sourced is a 99.99% organic. Grow the plant yourself and make it 100%)

If your hair is very short, just rub a little oil such as rosehip or sweet almond into hair and ruffle it up.

3.9   Naked Soap Co website and email address

www.nakedsoap.ie

nakedsoapco@eircom.net

Appendix 4

Favourite Easy Healthy Recipes

Toasted wholemeal pitta bread

Stuffed with as many as possible of the following (preferably organic):

Shredded lettuce, grated carrot, sliced boiled free-range egg, sliced spring onion (scallion), seed/bean sprouts, sliced tomato, watercress, sliced orange and red pepper (capsicum), seeds, nuts

Healthy salad

Shredded iceberg lettuce, shredded cos (romaine) lettuce, shredded little gem lettuce, red lettuce, grated carrot, sliced red and orange peppers, whole grain rice, radishes, sliced red onion, sliced spring onion (scallion), beetroot, sunflower seeds, pumpkin seeds, walnuts,

Prawns Chinese style

Cook a pot of wholegrain rice (don't overcook, whole grain rice is more 'nutty' than white rice). Add a little Chinese 5 spice.

Stir fry a selection of the following (don't overcook, leave vegetables crunchy):

Chunky onion slices, sliced spring onion, sliced carrot, sliced mushrooms, mange tout, sugarsnap peas, baby sweetcorn, sliced peppers (red, orange, yellow), bean sprouts, any other sprouts you can buy or make. Add pre cooked prawns and a handful of cashew nuts, continue to stir fry until hot.

Serve stir fry vegetables on rice, and top with sweet and sour or plum sauce.

For an added treat, add oven baked spring rolls. Yum.

Alternatively add diced cooked turkey or chicken breast instead of cooked prawns.

Mediterranean Vegetables

Stir fry the following vegetables slowly in a little olive oil and a sprinkling of mixed herbs: Sliced courgettes or baby marrow, chunky mushrooms, cherry tomatoes, sliced aubergine, sliced red pepper (capsicum), chunky onions slices.

Appendix 5

References and Bibliography

1. Bauby, J.D., 1977, *The Diving Bell and the Butterfly*, Harper-Collins Press

2. Olivier, S., 2003, *The Breast Cancer Prevention and Recovery Diet*, 3rd edition, London, Penguin Books Ltd

3. Erasmus, U., 1993, *Fats that Kill, Fats that Heal*, chapter 17, Alive Books, Burnaby BC, Canada

4. Health Physics Society, 2002, *Microwaves, Radar, and Radiofrequency — Microwaves and Radiofrequency*, available at http://www.hps.org/publicinformation/ate/q1913.html accessed 02.02.08

5. Naturalnews.com, 2005, *Nurses Recommend Aluminium-Free Deodorants*, available at http://www.naturalnews.com/009969.html accessed 12.08.08

6. Natural Health Information Centre, *The potential implication of SLS and SLES on Human Health*, available at http://www.natural-health-information-centre.com/sls-health-implications.html accessed 17.12.08

7. Journal of Clinical Oncology, 2006, *X-rays may boost breast cancer risk by 250%*, available at http://www.naturalnews.com/019477.html accessed 02.02.08

8. Health.Yahoo.Com, 2007, *Phototherapy for psoriasis*, available at http://health.yahoo.com/skinconditions-treatment/phototherapy-for-psoriasis/healthwise--hw57899.html accessed 2.2.08

9. The New Zealand Herald, 2006, *Apricot kernels carry risk of cyanide poisoning*, available at http://www.nzherald.co.nz/section/1/story.cfm?c_id=1&ObjectID=10379786 accessed 15.02.08

10. Cancer-Healing.Com, *Laetrile's (Amygdalin) Mode of Action*, available at http://www.cancer-healing.com/cancer_b17.php accessed 17.12.08

11. Irish Cancer Society, 2007, *Understanding Cancer and Complementary Therapies*, Irish Cancer Society, 43 – 45 Northumberland Road, Dublin 4

12. Mills, L., 2007, *In your face*, Penguin Ireland, 25 St Stephen's Green, Dublin 2

13. Health24.com 2007, *Oestrogen*, available at http://www.health24.com/medical/Condition_centres/ 777-792-819-1807,16862.asp accessed 19.12.08

14. No Ho Arts District.com, *Writing for the Artist as Therapy*, available at http://www.nohoartsdistrict.com/literary_arts/how_to _writing_therapy.htm accessed 06.07.08

15. BBC News, 2008, *Writing 'eases stress of cancer'*, available at http://news.bbc.co.uk/2/hi/health/7304294.stm accessed 06.07.08

226

Further copies of this book are available from

Susan Connell-Ford
Glendalough
The Nire Valley
Ballymacarbry
Co Waterford
Ireland

Cheques/postal orders payable to
Susan Connell-Ford
€13.50/£12.50 (Ireland and Northern Ireland)
€16/£15 (Rest of the World)
Includes cost of postage and packing

Price correct at time of going to print but current
price can be checked on the naked soap website
shown below or by emailing
anna4d@iol.ie

Or pay through paypal at
www.nakedsoap.ie/themword.html